Mathematics
for the Digital Age

Programming
in Python

>>> Second Edition:
    with Python 3

Maria Litvin

Phillips Academy, Andover, Massachusetts

Gary Litvin

Skylight Software, Inc.

Skylight Publishing
Andover, Massachusetts

Skylight Publishing
9 Bartlet Street, Suite 70
Andover, MA 01810

web: http://www.skylit.com
e-mail: sales@skylit.com
          support@skylit.com

Library of Congress Control Number: 2009913596

ISBN 978-0-9824775-4-0

3 4 5 6 7 8 9   22 21 20 19

Printed in the United States of America

Brief Contents

About the Authors

Maria Litvin has taught mathematics and computer science at Phillips Academy in Andover, Massachusetts, since 1987. She is an Advanced Placement Computer Science exam reader and, as a consultant for The College Board, provides AP training for high school computer science teachers. Maria is a recipient of the 1999 Siemens Award for Advanced Placement for Mathematics, Science, and Technology for New England and of the 2003 RadioShack National Teacher Award. Prior to joining Phillips Academy, Maria taught computer science at Boston University. Maria is a co-author of *C++ for You++: An Introduction to Programming and Computer Science*, which became one of the leading high school textbooks for AP Computer Science courses, and *Java Methods A & AB*. Maria is also the author of *Be Prepared for the AP Computer Science Exam in Java*.

Gary Litvin is a co-author of *C++ for You++*, *Java Methods*, and *Be Prepared for the AP Computer Science Exam in Java*. Gary is also the author of *Solutions to 800 Questions in Calculus* and the editor of *Be Prepared for the AP Calculus Exam*. Gary has worked in many areas of software development including artificial intelligence, pattern recognition, computer graphics, and neural networks. As founder of Skylight Software, Inc., he developed SKYLIGHTS/GX, one of the first visual programming tools for C and C++ programmers. Gary led in the development of several state-of-the-art software products including interactive touch screen development tools, OCR and handwritten character recognition systems, and credit card fraud detection software.

Contents

How to Use This Book

The *Math and Python* companion web site —

    http://www.skylit.com/python

— is an integral part of this book. It contains downloadable student files for exercises, assembled together in what we call *Student Disk*. Also on the book's web site are some of the appendices, links, errata, supplemental papers and syllabi, and technical support information for teachers.

Py refers to the *Math and Python Student Disk*. For example, "The file of words, words.txt, is provided in Py\Ch09" means the words.txt file is located in the Ch09 subfolder in your Student Disk folder.

 This icon draws your attention to a hands-on exploration of an example.

 "Parentheses" like these, in the margin, mark supplementary material intended for a more inquisitive reader. This material either gives a glimpse of things to come in subsequent chapters or adds technical details.

1.■, 2.◆ In exercises, a square indicates an "intermediate" question that may require more thought or work than an ordinary question or exercise. A diamond indicates an "advanced" question that could be treacherous or lead to unexplored territory or take a lot of work.

✓ A checkmark at the end of a question in exercises means that the answer or a solution is included on your student disk. We have included answers and solutions to about one-third of the exercises. They can be found in Py\SolutionsToExercises (click on index.html).

Teacher Disk, which contains complete solutions to all the exercises and labs, is available for downloading free of charge to teachers who use this book as a textbook in their school. Go to skylit.com/python and click on the "Teachers' Room" link for details.

Preface

"So, is this a math book or a computer programming book?" This is probably the first question on the impatient reader's mind. But why should it be? It is a librarian's dilemma: Does it go on the math shelf or on the computer shelf? There is a simple solution: put a copy on each.

The purpose of this book is to teach a particular way of thinking — precision thinking — and how to solve problems that require this way of thinking. Both mathematics and computer programming nourish the ability to think with precision and to solve problems that call for exact solutions.

Mathematics teaches us to appreciate the beauty of a rigorous argument. In the long run, this is more valuable than a lesson on solving today's practical problems. Still, mathematics does not exist in a vacuum — its abstractions are rooted in practical knowledge accumulated over centuries. The teaching of mathematics draws on examples and analogies from the world around us. At least, it should. However, the world around us is changing more and more rapidly. In the past 50 or 60 years, our world has changed dramatically: it has gone digital. This change is so profound that it is sometimes hard to fully comprehend. Is that why the change remains largely ignored in our K-12 math curricula? We need to start filling the gap.

If we could build a time machine and bring Euclid over for a visit, he would find it comforting amid the chaos of modern technologies that geometry familiar to him is still taught in schools. Old rivals Newton and Leibniz would both find great satisfaction in the fact that tens of thousands of 11th and 12th graders are learning how to take derivatives and use integrals. But George Boole, a visitor from the more recent past, would have to search through dozens of school textbooks before he could find his algebra of propositions mentioned even in passing, despite the fact that his name is immortalized in every modern computer programming language. As for John von Neumann, a brilliant mathematician and one of the fathers of computer technology... well, with his usual optimism he would predict that within 20 years or so, every elementary school student will learn about the AND, OR, and NOT gates. And why not?

In this book we have collected some of the easier mathematical topics that are relevant to the digital world. Many of these topics are often bundled together in freshman college courses under the name *discrete mathematics*. Discrete mathematics has become a euphemism for all elementary mathematics that is relevant today but neglected in standard middle and high school algebra, precalculus, and calculus courses. In the 1970s, Donald Knuth and his colleagues at Stanford coined the phrase "concrete mathematics" — a blend of CONtinuous and disCRETE mathematics (and also solid and not too abstract) — to describe the course Knuth taught at Stanford. Later, *Concrete Mathematics* became the title of their delightful book.[1]   As they explain in the preface, Knuth "had found that there were mathematical tools missing from his repertoire; the mathematics he needed for a thorough, well grounded understanding of computer programs was quite different from what he'd learned as a mathematics major in college."

We believe that starting in college is too late. Many concepts are completely accessible to middle and high school students. And there is also another side to the relationship: just as mathematics helps achieve a deeper understanding of computer programs, some hands-on experience with computer programming helps make mathematics more tangible, familiar, and easier to grasp.

So, if you are interested mainly in computers, we hope this book will make you a better computer programmer. If you are more interested in math, you will have ample opportunities to solve interesting problems and model some of them in computer programs. You will become familiar with fun areas of mathematics that are usually kept from middle and high school students for no obvious reason; you will learn to solve real problems (that is, problems that you don't already know how to "solve" ahead of time); you will learn the power of mathematical reasoning and proof. As a bonus, you will acquire the practical skill of programming in Python, a popular commercial programming language.

We chose Python for several reasons. First, Python gives you a chance to experiment with the language in an interactive setting with immediate feedback. Second, Python's syntax is not too complicated. Third, Python has simple but powerful features for working with lists and "dictionaries" (maps). Finally, Python is easy to install and get started with, and it's free. Of course, there are other programming languages that have similar properties and would meet our needs. In the end, it is not any particular programming language that matters, but the ability to think with precision about both mathematical facts and computer programs.

---

[1] Ronald L. Graham, Donald E. Knuth, Oren Patashnik, *Concrete Mathematics: A Foundation for Computer Science*, Second Edition, Addison-Wesley, 1998.

We are very grateful to Dr. J. Adrian Zimmer of the Oklahoma School of Science and Mathematics for sharing his ideas about teaching math and Python. Adrian read a draft of this book and made valuable suggestions and corrections.

We thank Kenneth S. Oliver (formerly of Amity Regional High School in Woodbridge, Connecticut) for taking the time to read a draft very thoroughly, pointing out mistakes, and helping to clarify some explanations.

We are very grateful to Prof. Duncan A. Buell, Chair of the Department of Computer Science and Engineering at University of South Carolina in Columbia, for reading a draft and suggesting improvements and corrections, especially for the Number Theory and Cryptology chapter (Chapter 17).

Our thanks to Benjamin Niedzielski, Phillips Academy '08, for writing solutions to many exercises.

In the second edition, Python code in all examples and exercises has been converted to Python 3. According to Python developers,

> Python 3.0, also known as 'Python 3000' or 'Py3K', is the first ever intentionally backwards-incompatible Python release. There are more changes than in a typical release, and more that are important for all Python users. Nevertheless, after digesting the changes, you'll find that Python really hasn't changed all that much – by and large, we're mostly fixing well-known annoyances and warts, and removing a lot of old cruft.[*]

We have inserted the "Parity, Invariants, and Finite Strategy Games" chapter after Chapter 9 and split the Graphs chapter into two, adding sections on graph coloring and the Four Color Theorem.

---

[*] See http://docs.python.org/3.1/whatsnew/3.0.html.

1 Sets and Functions

1.1 Prologue

A *function* establishes a relation between a *set* of inputs (numbers, points, objects) and a set of outputs.

> **A function associates one output with each input.**

But the same output can be associated with two or more different inputs (Figure 1-1).

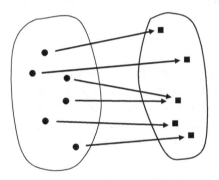

Figure 1-1. A function associates one output with each input

The concept of function is essential for most branches of mathematics and science. A function defines a relationship between objects or quantities, and that is precisely what math and science are concerned with: how things relate to each other.

We often use lowercase letters as names for functions. Given a function f, we often use the letter x to denote the function's input. We call the corresponding output $f(x)$. In other words, a function f maps an input x onto the output $f(x)$.

> **A function is also called a *mapping*: it maps the set of inputs into the set of outputs.**

▌ **The input value passed to a function is called its *argument*.**

In this chapter we will discuss different ways to define a function and at the end experiment with simple Python functions.

1.2   Sets

A set of inputs... A set of outputs... You might be wondering: What exactly is a "set"? The concept of a *set* is one of those fundamental mathematical concepts that cannot be defined formally. A set is... well, any collection of things. For example, a set of all the students in the classroom, a set of all the letters in the alphabet, a set of all positive integers under 10.

▌ **The items that belong to a set are called its *elements*.**

$x \in S$ means x is an element of the set S.

A set can have a finite number of elements — such a set is called a *finite set*. For a finite set, we can list all its elements (although it may take some time if the set is large, such as the set of all Chinese characters). A set can have only one element. For convenience, mathematicians also define the *empty set* — a set that has no elements at all. The notation for the empty set is $\varnothing$.

With a little imagination, we can also define *infinite sets*. For example, a set of all positive integers, a set of all points on a straight line, a set of all finite sets of integers... We cannot list all the elements of an infinite set. Defining an infinite set can be tricky: infinite sets exist only in the abstract realm of mathematics.

We will use uppercase letters as names for sets and use curly braces to list the elements of a set. For example, $A = \{1, 2, 3\}$ states that the set A contains the three elements, 1, 2, and 3. $\mathbb{N} = \{1, 2, 3, \dots\}$ represents the set of all positive integers; $\mathbb{R}$ represents the set of all real numbers. (We couldn't possibly list all the elements of $\mathbb{R}$.)

If the set B is made up of some of the elements of the set A, then B is called a *subset* of A. The notation $B \subseteq A$ means B is a subset of A. For example, $\{2, 3\} \subseteq \{1, 2, 3\}$. For any set S, $\varnothing \subseteq S$ and $S \subseteq S$.

> **The set of all the possible inputs of a function *f* is called the *domain* of *f*.**
> **The set of all the outputs of *f* is called the *range* of *f*.**

If *x* is an element of the domain of *f*, then $f(x)$ is an element of the range of *f*.

Example 1

Let *Z* be the set of all integers and *E* the set of all even integers. The function that takes any integer *n* as input and returns 2*n* as the output maps *Z* onto *E*:

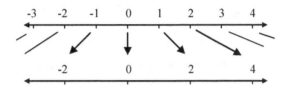

If we call this function *g*, we can say that $g(n) = 2n$. *Z* is the domain of *g*. *E* is the range of *g*.

Example 2

$A = \{0, 1, 2\}$ is a set of three elements. The function $0 \rightarrow 1, \ 1 \rightarrow 2, \ 2 \rightarrow 0$ maps *A* onto itself. *A* is both the domain and the range of this function.

It is often convenient to view the range of a function as a subset of a larger set (Figure 1-2).

We can say that a function *maps* its domain <u>onto</u> its range and <u>into</u> a larger set that contains the range. This way, if you have two sets, *A* and *B*, you can consider all functions from *A* <u>into</u> *B*; for each such function its range is a subset of *B* (possibly equal to the whole set *B*).

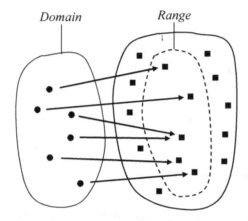

Figure 1-2. The range of a function can be a subset of a larger set

Example 3

Suppose *P* is the set of all the students in the classroom, and the function *birthday*(*p*) takes a person *p* as its input and returns *p*'s birthday as the output. It is convenient to view this as a mapping from the set *P* (all students in the classroom) <u>into</u> the set *D* (all 366 possible birthdays, including February 29 for those special people who were born on that day in a leap year). The range of the function *birthday* — the days on which the actual birthdays of the students in the classroom happen to fall — is a subset of *D*.

Exercises

1. $T = \{a, b\}$ is a set of two elements. List all the different subsets of T. How many are there? (Be sure to include the empty set and the subset that is the whole set T.) ✓

2.   How many different subsets does a set of three elements have? A set of four elements? A set of n elements?

3.   Give an example of a function whose domain has five elements and whose range has five elements. ✓

4.   Can you define a function whose domain has three elements and whose range has two elements? If yes, give an example; if not, explain why not.

5.   Can you define a function whose domain has three elements and whose range has four elements? If yes, give an example; if not, explain why not.

6.   Give an example of a function whose domain is the set of all integers and whose range has three elements. ✓

7. A is a set of 17 elements, and a function f is defined on A (that is, A is f's domain). What is the smallest and the largest possible number of elements in f's range?

8.■   Suppose a set A has three elements and a set B has three elements. How many different functions from A into B can be defined? ✓

9.   Give an example of a function that maps all integers onto the set of all odd integers.

10.   Devise a function that has the set of all the English words as its domain and a set of all the letters of the English alphabet as its range.

11.   Devise a function that maps the set of all the points inside (and on the border) of a circle of radius 1 onto the set of real numbers $0 \le y \le 1$. ✓

12.■ Devise a function whose domain is the set of real numbers x such that $0 < x \le 1$ and whose range is the set of real numbers y such that $y \ge 1$.

1.3   Ways to Define a Function

To define a function you need to define its domain and a way to find or calculate the function's value (that is, the function's "output") for each element in the domain. There are several ways to define a function: in words, in a table, in a graph or a chart, or using a formula.

Example 1

A function defined in words:

"For any positive integer n, let $s(n)$ be the sum of all integers from 1 to n."

The domain of this function is all positive integers, and we can calculate the value of $s(n)$ for any n: $s(1) = 1$, $s(2) = 1 + 2 = 3$, $s(3) = 1 + 2 + 3 = 6$, and so on.

Example 2

Suppose we say something like this: "$f(year)$ is the number of fatal accidents in the U.S. caused by drunk drivers in a given year for the years between 1990 and 1999." This sentence describes the function in general terms, but does not give us its values. To complete the definition, we need to look up the data and arrange it in a table and/or a graph:

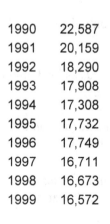

1990	22,587
1991	20,159
1992	18,290
1993	17,908
1994	17,308
1995	17,732
1996	17,749
1997	16,711
1998	16,673
1999	16,572

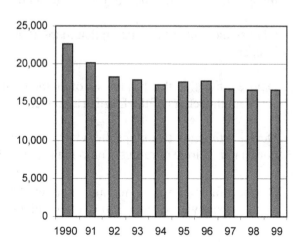

In math and physics, by far the most common and useful way to define a function is with a formula.

Example 3

Suppose we drop a rock from a cliff. The vertical distance it travels in t seconds is given by the formula $h(t) = 16t^2$ (feet). The domain of this function is all non-negative real numbers: for any $t \geq 0$ (any time after we drop the rock), we can calculate the value of $h(t)$ from the formula. For example, $h(5) = 16 \cdot 25 = 400$ (feet). If we measure the time it takes the rock to reach the ground, we can find the height of the cliff.

It is often convenient to agree ahead of time on a "universal set" on which we consider functions, for example, the set $\mathbb{R}$ of all real numbers, or the set of all points on a plane (for plane geometry), or the set of all integers (for number theory). The domains of all functions we consider are then subsets of that universal set. We have to also agree on the "universal set" to which the outputs of the functions belong.

Suppose we are working with real numbers and functions whose values are also real numbers, so both the domain and the range of a function are subsets of $\mathbb{R}$. We can write a formula, for example $f(x) = \dfrac{1}{x}$. This formula makes sense (that is, $f(x)$ can be calculated) for all $x \neq 0$, so it defines a function with the domain "all real numbers except 0" (or, in mathematical notation, $\mathbb{R} - \{0\}$).

If we define a function by a formula and do not specify the domain explicitly, it is assumed that the domain is the set of all numbers for which the formula makes sense.

This is called the *natural domain* of a function defined by a formula.

Example 4

For a real number x, $\sqrt{x}$ makes sense (produces a real number) if and only if $x \geq 0$. Therefore, the natural domain of the function defined by the formula $f(x) = \sqrt{x}$ is the set of all non-negative real numbers. (The range of this function is also all non negative real numbers.)

Sometimes the same function can be described in two different ways. When we prove that two definitions describe the same function, we usually obtain an interesting mathematical fact. Consider for example the function described in Example 1: for any positive integer n, let $s(n)$ be the sum of all integers from 1 to n. Consider another function, defined by the formula $f(n) = \dfrac{n(n+1)}{2}$. Let us <u>prove</u> that $s(n)$ and $f(n)$ actually represent the same function: that is, for any positive integer n, $s(n) = f(n)$.

You may be tempted to take a few values of n and compare $s(n)$ with $f(n)$. For example, for $n = 2$, $1 + 2 = \dfrac{2 \cdot 3}{2} = 3$; for $n = 5$, $1 + 2 + 3 + 4 + 5 = \dfrac{5 \cdot 6}{2} = 15$. This indicates that we are on the right track, but it is <u>not</u> a mathematical proof. How can we be sure that this property holds for <u>every</u> positive integer n? There are infinitely many possible values of n, and we cannot check every one of them.

> **In a mathematical proof, we have to show that the fact is true beyond any doubt.**

A mathematical proof of the fact that $s(n) = f(n)$ for any positive integer n can go like this. By definition,

$$s(n) = \quad 1 \quad + \quad 2 \quad + \quad \ldots \quad + \quad (n-1) \quad + \quad n$$

Let us rewrite this sum in reverse order (we know that the result of addition does not depend on the order of the operands — there is a postulate or a theorem to that effect):

$$s(n) = \quad n \quad + \quad (n-1) \quad + \quad \ldots \quad + \quad 2 \quad + \quad 1$$

Now let us add the two lines together termwise (the term above plus the term below):

$$
\begin{array}{ccccccccc}
\boxed{\begin{array}{l} s(n) = 1 \\ s(n) = n \end{array}} & + & \boxed{\begin{array}{l} 2 \\ (n-1) \end{array}} & + & \dots & + & \boxed{\begin{array}{l} (n-1) \\ 2 \end{array}} & + & \boxed{\begin{array}{l} n \\ 1 \end{array}}
\end{array}
$$

We get:

$$
2 \cdot s(n) = \underbrace{n+1 \quad + \quad n+1 \quad + \quad \dots \quad + \quad n+1 \quad + \quad n+1}_{n \text{ times}}
$$

Therefore, $2 \cdot s(n) = n(n+1)$ and $s(n) = \dfrac{n(n+1)}{2}$, Q.E.D. (This is from Latin: Quod Erat Demonstrandum — what we needed to show.)

❖ ❖ ❖

Ideally, a mathematical proof should follow from the most basic agreed-on assumptions (*postulates*) or from facts that have already been proven earlier (*theorems*). It would be way too tedious, though, to do that for every proof. So mathematicians often skip the earlier steps that depend on established mathematical facts. The above proof is an example of that. Mathematicians know that someone somewhere had worked out the needed steps down to the postulates.

Exercises

1.   What is the natural domain of the function defined for real numbers by the formula $f(x) = \dfrac{1}{x-2}$? What is the range of this function? ✓

2.   What is the natural domain of $f(x) = \sqrt{1+x}$? What is the range?

3.◆   What is the natural domain of $f(x) = \sqrt{1-x^2}$? What is the range?

4.   Consider a function defined on the set of all three-digit positive integers; for each integer, the function returns the sum of its digits. For example, $f(243) = 9$. How many elements do the domain and the range of this function have? ✓

5.■   The table below shows a few values of the function $h(n)$ defined on the set of all positive integers:

n	1	2	3	4	5	6
$h(n)$	2	5	10	17	26	37

Come up with a simple formula that matches the function for the values shown in the table.

6.   Describe a function f whose domain and range are both the set of all the points on a plane and that has exactly one *fixed point*, that is, a point P such that $f(P) = P$.

7.   Given a set A of three elements, how many functions from A onto itself (that is, such functions that both the domain and the range of the function is A) have no fixed points? ✓

8.■   Come up with a formula that defines a function on $\mathbb{R}$ with the natural domain $-1 < x < 1$ and the range $\mathbb{R}$.

9.■   Consider the functions f and g, defined by the following tables:

x	-1	0	1
$f(x)$	3	1	-1

x	-1	0	1
$g(x)$	-2	-1	0

What are the values of $f(g(1))$ and $g(f(1))$?

10.◆   Consider the following function d defined for all positive integers: $d(n)$ is the sum of all <u>odd</u> positive integers below $2n$. Prove that for any positive n, $d(n) = n^2$.

1.4   Algorithms

Another way to define a function is to describe an algorithm or to write a computer program for calculating its values.

> An *algorithm* is a precise description of the steps necessary to calculate a function or to accomplish a certain task.

A recipe in a cookbook is a type of algorithm. But "interesting" algorithms usually involve several steps that are repeated many times. This allows us to "fold" a long sequence of steps into a relatively short algorithm — which gives algorithms their power.

Example 1

The following algorithm takes a positive integer *n* and returns the number of digits in it:

> Set *count* to 1
> Set *power* to 10
> While *power* $\leq n$, repeat the following steps:
>   Increment *count* by 1
>   Multiply *power* by 10
> Return *count*

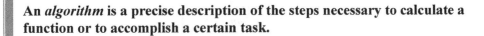

Algorithms are often described not in words but in a more concise notation, called *pseudocode*. In pseudocode the above algorithm might look like this:

```
count ← 1
power ← 10
while power ≤ n:
    count ← count + 1
    power ← power * 10
return count
```

Pseudocode is not a computer language, so the algorithm above is not real computer "code" — it is less formalized. But we could easily *implement* this pseudocode algorithm in many programming languages.

❖   ❖   ❖

Another way to describe an algorithm is with a *flowchart*. A flowchart for the above algorithm might look like this:

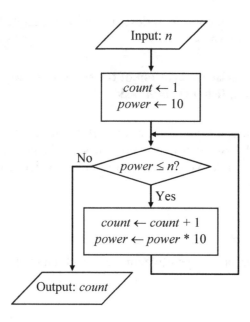

Flowcharts belong in a computer museum — they are hardly used nowadays.

Example 2

Let $p(n)$ be the largest k such that n is evenly divisible by 2^k (that is, the remainder when n is divided by 2^k is 0). For example, $p(3) = 0$, $p(6) = 1$, $p(8) = 3$, $p(12) = 2$, and $p(14) = 1$. It might seem, at first, that the only way to calculate $p(n)$ is to try every value of 2^k less than or equal to n, take the largest of them, and return the corresponding k. However, it turns out there is a more economical algorithm:

Set k to 0
While n is even, repeat the following steps:
    Add 1 to k
    Divide n by 2
Return k

The same in pseudocode:

```
k ← 0
while n is even:
    k ← k + 1
    n ← n/2
return k
```

Exercises

1.   Name a couple of algorithms that you know from arithmetic and algebra.

2.   Devise an algorithm for calculating $s(n) = 1 + 2 + ... + n$ without using the

formula $s(n) = \dfrac{n(n+1)}{2}$. Present your algorithm in pseudocode.

3.   Suppose you only have the operations of addition and subtraction. Devise an algorithm that takes two positive integers, m and n, and calculates the quotient and the remainder when m is divided by n. (For example, when 17 is divided by 5, the quotient is 3 and the remainder is 2.) Present your algorithm in pseudocode. ✓

4.■   Devise an algorithm for calculating 3^n, where n is a non-negative integer. Write your algorithm in pseudocode.

5.■   Devise an algorithm that for a given positive integer n finds the largest integer k such that $2^k \leq n$. Write pseudocode and draw a flowchart for this algorithm.

6.♦   Suppose `word` is a string of letters (all lower case). Suppose `word[i]` refers to the i-th letter of `word` (starting from 0: `word[0]` is the first letter of `word`). Suppose `len(word)` refers to the number of letters in `word`. Devise an algorithm that compares two words and decides which one goes first in a dictionary. ✓

1.5   Exploring Functions in Python

In Chapter 2, we will talk about computer programs and programming languages. Meanwhile, we can start playing with Python a little. Don't worry if you don't understand all the technical notation right away. You'll get used to it very soon. Meanwhile, just follow along and see what you notice. When you start to write your own little programs in the exercises, just copy the format of the sample programs.

> **If you haven't done so already, go ahead and download Python and other tools from `www.python.org`. This book's web site, `www.skylit.com/python`, has instructions for getting started with Python: downloading the interpreter and running programs (Appendix A).**

Like almost all programming languages, Python allows you to define functions. The concept of a function in a program is similar to the concept of a function in math: a function in Python can take an input (one or more arguments) and return an output (the result). You can also view a function as a fragment of program code that can be called from different places in the program, with different arguments.

Example 1

Start the Python interpreter and type:

```
>>> def double(n):
        return 2*n
```

This defines a function, called `double`, which returns its argument multiplied by 2. `def` is a *reserved word* in Python (a word with a special meaning in a programming language). `def` indicates that we are defining a function. Note the colon at the end of the "def" line: it is required by Python's *syntax rules*. Statements within the function definition are *indented* (shifted to the right, here by four spaces). `return` is another Python reserved word — it indicates what value the function *returns* to the caller.

Once a function is defined, you can *call* it with different arguments:

```
>>> double(3)
6
>>> double(0.5)
1.0
```

❖   ❖   ❖

In the above example, we named our function "double." This self-explanatory name indicates what the function computes. We could have called it "*s*" or "*f*" or "*d*", as we do in math — Python doesn't care. But imagine a program with dozens of functions named *f, g, a, z, s,...* Even the author would have trouble remembering which function does what. And other programmers would find such a program totally incomprehensible.

> **When you are writing a computer program, always keep in mind that you are writing it not only for yourself, but also for others to read.**

Choose meaningful names for functions, even if they take longer to type — never be stingy with keystrokes.

In a program, a definition of a function can do much more than just return a value of an expression (formula). A function can implement an algorithm for computing a value.

Example 2

Here is a Python function for computing the function $p(n)$ from Example 2 in Section 1.4. $p(n)$ returns the largest k, such that n is evenly divisible by 2^k. This Python code corresponds to the algorithm discussed in that example, but instead of calling this function "p" we have called it "largestPower2Divisor." Notice the *comments* set off by the # sign — the computer doesn't read them, but they help the reader of the program to follow what's going on:

```
>>> def largestPower2Divisor(n):
        k = 0
        while n % 2 == 0:      # while n is even
            k += 1             #    k <- k + 1
            n //= 2            #    n <- n // 2 --
                               #      divide and truncate to an int
        return k
```

You can test this function by calling it with different arguments:

```
>>> largestPower2Divisor(6)
1
>>> largestPower2Divisor(8)
3
>>> largestPower2Divisor(12)
2
>>> largestPower2Divisor(14)
1
```

Exercises

1. Type in the function

```
def mod3(n):
    return n % 3
```

and call it with various integer arguments. Can you figure out what the `%` operator means in Python? How does it work for positive and negative integers?

2. Define a function `incrementByOne` that takes an argument x and returns $x+1$. Test your function for $x=3$, $x=-5$, and $x=1.5$. ✓

3. Python has a number of built-in (predefined) functions. One of them is called `abs`. Try calling this function with various arguments and figure out what it returns.

4. Define a Python function `sum1ToN` that returns $1+2+...+n$ using the formula $1+2+...+n=\dfrac{n(n+1)}{2}$. Test your function for several values of n.

≈ Hint: You can omit the multiplication sign in algebraic expressions, but not in Python! Use `//` for division so that the function returns an integer. ≈

5. Define a function `reciprocal(x)` that returns `1/x`. Try calling it for $x=0$. How does Python deal with natural domains of functions? ✓

6. Suppose you have defined the functions `double` (from Example 1) and `incrementByOne` from Question 2. What is the result of `double(incrementByOne(5))`? What is the result of `incrementByOne(double(5))`? Explain these results.

7.   In Python, a word, a phrase, or any string of letters, digits, or other characters written within single or double quotes represents a *literal string*: an object whose <u>value</u> is that string of characters. For example, `'Hello, World!'` represents a string whose value is "Hello, World!". Try calling the function `incrementByOne` from Question 2 with the argument `'123'`. Can you add a number to a string in Python?

8.   Call the function `double` from Example 1 with the argument `'123'`. What does Python's `*` operator do when one operand is an integer and the other is a string? ✓

9.   In Python, if `s` is a string, `s[0]` refers to its first character. Define and test a function that takes a word and returns its first character. ✓

10.   In Python, `[a, b, c, ..., x]` represents a list of objects. For example, `[1, 5, 2]` represents a list of three numbers: 1, 5, and 2. What does the function defined in Question 9 return when, instead of a string, a list is passed to it as an argument?

11.   Question 10 describes how a list of numbers can be represented in Python. Experiment and find out what Python's built-in functions `sum`, `min`, and `max` do when applied to a list of numbers.

12.■   What do `min(range(n))` and `max(range(n))` return when `n` is a positive integer? ✓

13.■   Rewrite the function `sum1ToN` from Question 4 using only one + and no other arithmetic operators. ⸮ Hint: use two of Python's built-in functions; see Questions 11 and 12. ⸮

14.◆   Using the function from Example 2 as a prototype, write a function `numDigits` that returns the number of digits in a positive integer. The algorithm is described in Example 1 in Section 1.4 ⸮ Hint: the statement

```
while p <= n:
```

will repeat the statements indented below it as long as `p` remains less than or equal to `n`. ⸮

1.6   Review

Terms and notation introduced in this chapter:

Set	*Range*	$A = \{a, b, c\}$
Finite set	*Argument*	$x \in A$
Infinite set	*Natural domain*	$\varnothing$
Subset	*Algorithm*	$A \subseteq B$
Empty set	*Pseudocode*	$f(x)$
Function	*Flowchart*	
Mapping	*Reserved word*	
Domain	*Literal string*	

Some of the Python features mentioned in this chapter:

reserved words `def` and `return`

`+` operator

`*` operator

`%` operator

Single or double quotes designate literal strings, as in `'Hello'` or `"Hello"`.

Square brackets designate a list of objects, as in `[a, b, c]`

Built-in functions: `abs`, `sum`, `max`, `min`, `range`

2 An Introduction to Programming

2.1 Prologue

For a casual computer user, a computer program is something that comes on a CD or is downloaded from the Internet, and then runs on the computer screen — not unlike a TV show, except that the user has some control over what happens. For a programmer, a program is a set of instructions that the computer executes to perform precisely defined tasks. Actually, computer programming is much more than just "coding" these instructions — it involves many skills, including software design, devising algorithms, designing *user interfaces* (screens, commands, menus, toolbars, etc.), writing and testing code, and interacting with the users of software.

2.2 CPU and Memory

At the heart of a computer is the *Central Processing Unit* (*CPU*). In a personal computer, the CPU is a microprocessor made from a tiny chip of silicon. The chip has millions of *transistors* etched on it. A transistor is a microscopic digital switch: it controls two states of a signal, "on" or "off," "1" or "0." The microprocessor is protected by a small ceramic case mounted on a *printed circuit board* called the *motherboard*. Also on the motherboard are memory chips.

The computer memory is a uniform pool of storage units called *bytes*.

One byte holds eight bits.

A bit stores the smallest possible unit of information: "1" or "0", "true" or "false."

A CPU does not have to read or write memory bytes sequentially: bytes can be accessed in any order. This is why computer memory is called *random-access memory* or *RAM*). The same memory is used to store different types of information: numbers, letters, sounds, images, programs, and so on. All these things must be encoded, one way or another, as sequences of 0s and 1s.

A typical personal computer made in the year 2009 had 2 to 4 "gigs" (gigabytes) of RAM.

> **1** *kilobyte* **(*KB*) = 1024 bytes = 2^{10} bytes, approximately one thousand bytes.**
> **1** *megabyte* **(*MB*) = 1024 kilobytes = 2^{20} bytes = 1,048,576 bytes, approximately one million bytes.**
> **1** *gigabyte* **(*GB*) = 1024 megabytes = 2^{30} bytes = 1,073,741,824 bytes, approximately one billion bytes.**
> **1** *terabyte* **(*TB*) = 1024 gigabytes = 2^{40} bytes.**

The CPU interprets and executes instructions stored in RAM. The CPU fetches the next instruction, interprets its operation code, and performs the appropriate operation. There are instructions for arithmetic and logical operations, for copying bytes from one location to another, and for changing the order of execution of instructions. The instructions are executed sequentially, unless a particular instruction tells the CPU to "jump" to another place in the program. *Conditional branching* instructions tell the CPU to continue with the next instruction or jump to another place depending on the result of the previous operation.

All this happens at amazing speeds. Each instruction takes one or several *clock cycles*, and a modern CPU runs at the speed of several GHz (gigahertz, that is, billion cycles per second).

To get a better feel for what CPU instructions are and how they are executed, let's consider a couple of examples. This will involve a brief glimpse of *Assembly Language*, the primitive computer language that underlies the modern languages you have heard of, such as C++, Java, and Python.

Example 1

The screen shot in Figure 2-1 shows a session with a program called *debug*. *debug* is an ancient program that was originally supplied with the MS-DOS operating system but still runs under *Windows*. *debug* allows a programmer to execute a program step by step, in a controlled manner, and examine the contents of memory at each step. This can help locate mistakes when the program is not working as expected. (Mistakes in computer code are called *bugs*, and the process of ridding a program of mistakes is called *debugging*.)

debug understands a few simple commands. The "a" command means "assemble": it allows you to type in a few CPU instructions. Here we've used it to enter a small segment of a computer program. These instructions are written in Assembly Language for the Intel 8088 microprocessor (which was used in the original IBM PC in the early 1980s), but they are still compatible with modern Intel CPUs. Assembly

Language is very close to the actual machine language, but it allows you to use mnemonic names, rather than digits, for instruction codes.

```
 Command Prompt                                                      _ □ ×
C:\mywork>debug
-a 0100
0AF9:0100 mov bx,0
0AF9:0103 mov ax,1
0AF9:0106 cmp ax,6
0AF9:0109 jg 0110
0AF9:010B add bx,ax
0AF9:010D inc ax
0AF9:010E jmp 0106
0AF9:0110 nop
0AF9:0111
-u 0100 0110
0AF9:0100 BB0000        MOV        BX,0000
0AF9:0103 B80100        MOV        AX,0001
0AF9:0106 3D0600        CMP        AX,0006
0AF9:0109 7F05          JG         0110
0AF9:010B 01C3          ADD        BX,AX
0AF9:010D 40            INC        AX
0AF9:010E EBF6          JMP        0106
0AF9:0110 90            NOP
-g =0100 0110

AX=0007  BX=0015  CX=0000  DX=0000  SP=FFEE  BP=0000  SI=0000  DI=0000
DS=0AF9  ES=0AF9  SS=0AF9  CS=0AF9  IP=0110     NV UP EI PL NZ NA PO NC
0AF9:0110 90            NOP
-q
```

Figure 2-1. A session with the *debug* program

The CPU has several temporary storage locations, called *registers*. The above code works with two registers, called AX and BX. For example, the first instruction that we typed in — mov bx, 0 — moves zero into the BX register.

After typing in the instructions, we verified our input by using *debug*'s "u" (unassemble) command. For each instruction, *debug* showed its address in memory, the instruction encoding, and the corresponding instruction in Assembly Language. The addresses and instruction codes are shown in "hex" (hexadecimal) system. We will explain the hexadecimal system in Chapter 5.

We then ran this code, using *debug*'s "g" ("go") command. We told it to start at the address 0100 and stop when it gets to address 0110. When done, the "g" command displayed the contents of all the CPU registers and the instruction that will be executed next. Here it is a NOP (no operation) instruction — an instruction that does nothing.

Below is the explanation of what each instruction in this code segment does:

```
  Hex        Hex              Assembly              Our
address   instruction        language            comment
             code            instruction

0AF9:0100 BB0000      ┌─► CMP  BX,0000 ; move 0 into the BX reg
0AF9:0103 B80100          MOV  AX,0001 ; move 1 into the AX reg
0AF9:0106 3D0600      ┌─► CMP  AX,0006 ; compare AX to 6
0AF9:0109 7F05        ├─┐ JG   0110    ; if greater, jump to 0110
0AF9:010B 01C3        │ │ ADD  BX,AX   ; add AX to BX
0AF9:010D 40          │ │ INC  AX      ; increment AX by 1
0AF9:010E EBF6        └─│ JMP  0106    ; jump back to 0106
0AF9:0110 90          └─► NOP          ; no operation -- skip
```

We leave it to you as an exercise (Question 7) to figure out what this code computes. The result is stored in the BX register.

Example 2

The Intel 8088 instruction set includes the call instruction, which emulates a call to a function. call saves the return address (the address of the instruction that follows call) on the *system stack* and passes control to the instruction at the specified address (the beginning of the function code). The program continues until it encounters the ret (return) instruction. ret fetches the return address from the system stack and passes control to the instruction at that address.

In the code below, the function starts at the address 0100. The AX register serves as the input, and the BX register serves as the output. This is a very simple function: the output is equal to input plus one:

```
0AF9:0100 mov bx,ax   ; move ax into bx
0AF9:0102 inc bx      ; increment bx
0AF9:0103 ret         ; return
```

We can call this function from another place in the program. For example:

```
0AF9:0106 mov ax,3
0AF9:0109 call 0100
```

When we execute these two instructions, we get

```
AX=0003  BX=0004  ...
```

If we execute

```
0AF9:010E mov ax,5
0AF9:0111 call 0100
```

we get

```
AX=0005  BX=0006  ...
```

Exercises

1. Find a discarded desktop computer, <u>make sure the power cord is unplugged</u>, and remove the cover. Identify the motherboard, CPU, and memory chips. Identify other components of the computer: power supply, hard disk, CD-ROM drive, and other components.

2. Computer memory is called RAM because: ✓

    A. It provides rapid access to data.
    B. It is mounted on the motherboard.
    C. It is measured in megabytes.
    D. Its bytes can be addressed in random order.
    E. Its chips are mounted in a rectangular array.

3. My old PC has 512 meg of RAM and a 120 gig hard drive. How many times more storage space does the hard disk have, as compared to RAM? ✓

4. How many different values can be encoded in 2 bits? 3 bits? 1 byte?

5. ASCII (read: 'as-kee) code represents upper- and lowercase letters of the English alphabet and other characters that you can find on a typical American keyboard. Each character is encoded in the same number of bits. Is one byte per character sufficient to represent all these characters? What is the smallest number of bits needed per character? ✓

6. In the program in Example 1, after we have issued the command

    ```
    -g =0100 0110
    ```

    how many times is the `cmp` instruction executed? ✓

7.■   Explain the contents of the AX and BX registers after the program segment in
        Example 1 has been executed. What does this code compute? ⅔ Hint: "hex"
        15 is decimal 21. ⅔

8.♦   In 8088 Assembly Language, you can give names to memory locations and
        then refer to them by name. For example:

```
v1     dw    5 ; reserve 2 bytes to hold an integer, call it v1
              ;    set its initial value to 5
v2     dw    6

...
mov    ax,v1
```

        You can also assign a label to a particular instruction and use it instead of the
        instruction address. For example:

```
L1:    cmp ax,bx
       ...
       jmp L1
```

        Write a segment of code that moves the larger of the values stored in
        memory locations v1 and v2 into the AX register. Your code should consist
        of four instructions. ⅔ Hint: in an 8088 CPU you can compare a memory
        location to a register, but you cannot compare two memory locations to each
        other in one instruction. ⅔

9.♦   Write a function in 8088 Assembly Language that takes the AX register as
        input and places its absolute value into BX, leaving AX unchanged. ⅔ Hint:
        8088 Assembly Language has the neg instruction, which negates the value in
        a register. ⅔

2.3 Python Interpreter

It would be extremely tedious to write programs as sequences of digits (although in
the very early days of the computer era, programmers did just that). Luckily, people
quickly realized that they could define special languages for writing programs and
use the computer itself to translate their programs from a high-level programming
language into machine code. Some early programming languages were FORTRAN,
COBOL, and BASIC. Some of the languages that are popular now are C++, C#,
Java, Perl, and Ruby. Python is another popular programming language; it was

created in the early 1990s by Guido van Rossum at Stichting Mathematisch Centrum in the Netherlands.

Using a high-level programming language, you can write statements that translate into several CPU instructions. Figure 2-2 shows a function written in Python.

```
def sum1ToN(n):
    "Returns 1 + 2 + ... + n"
    s = 0
    k = 1
    while k <= n:
        s += k    # add k to s
        k += 1    # increment k by 1
    return s
```

Figure 2-2. A function written in Python

A program written in a machine language or an Assembly Language works only on a computer with a compatible CPU. A program written in a high-level language can be used with any CPU. For example, it can run on a PC or on a Mac.

There are two ways to convert a program written in a high-level programming language into machine code. The first approach is called *compiling*: a special program, called a *compiler*, examines the text of the program, generates appropriate machine language instructions, and saves them in an executable file. Once a program is compiled, the compiler is not needed to run it. The second method is called *interpreting*: a special program, called an *interpreter*, examines the text of the program, generates the appropriate instructions, and executes these instructions right away. An interpreter does not create an executable file.

Compiling is like making a written translation of a text from a foreign language; interpreting is like doing a simultaneous interpretation while a foreign speaker is talking. An interpreter can read a program from a file, or it can allow you to enter program statements line by line, interactively.

Modern languages, such as Java and Python, use a hybrid approach. First they compile a program into an intermediate low-level language, called *bytecode*. Then they interpret the bytecode, which is still independent of a particular CPU, but is much more compact, closer to the machine language, and easier to interpret.

The text of a program is governed by rather rigid *syntax rules*: you can't just type whatever you want and expect the computer to understand it.

Every symbol in your program must be in just the right place.

In English or another natural language, you can misspell a word or omit a few punctuation marks and still produce a readable text. This is because natural languages have *redundancy*: information is transmitted with less than optimal efficiency, but this lets the reader interpret a message correctly even if it has been somewhat garbled (Figure 2-3).

Figure 2-3. A story by Lyla Fletcher Groom, age 5
Courtesy The Writing Workshop, www.writingworkshop.com.au

Programming languages have virtually no redundancy: almost every character is essential. There are many opportunities to make a mistake, so computer programmers have to learn patience and attention to detail.

We are now ready to experiment with Python. Python is available for free, even for commercial applications, under the *Open Source* license. The Python license is administered by the Python Software Foundation.

In a compiled language, you need to create the program text and save it in a file called *source code*, then run the source code file through a compiler to get an executable program. In Python, too, you can read a program from a source file. But you can also enter individual statements into the Python interpreter and see the result immediately.

Under *Windows*, it is more convenient to run the Python interpreter with a GUI (<u>G</u>raphical <u>U</u>ser <u>I</u>nterface) front end. It is called *IDLE* (Figure 2-4).

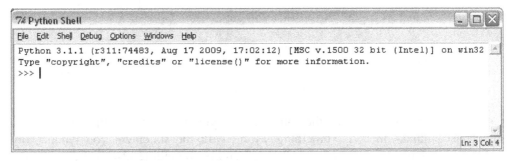

Figure 2-4.   Python GUI shell under *Windows*

>>> is the Python interpreter's prompt. A *prompt* is a signal from a program that it is waiting for user input. The user can type in a statement; when the user presses <Enter>, the interpreter displays the result. For example, type

```
>>> 2+2 <Enter>
```

(user input is shown in bold). Python will respond:

```
4
>>>
```

Looks reasonable! A number of things happen here. The interpreter reads the line of text (the statement) that you typed. It then analyzes the text and finds that the statement has two numbers (integers) separated by a + sign. The process of analyzing a text and extracting its components is called *parsing*.

A little experimentation will convince you that spaces do not matter (as long as the statement starts right after the prompt): you can type 2 + 2, 2 +2, or 2 +   2 — the result is the same. But if you type 2+*2, you will get

```
>>> 2+*2
      ^
SyntaxError: invalid syntax
>>>
```

Now try:

```
>>> 2(3+4)
```

You would expect 14, right? No! What you get is

```
Traceback (most recent call last):
  File "<pyshell#4>", line 1, in <module>
    2(3+4)
TypeError: 'int' object is not callable
```

Clearly Python (we will call the interpreter "Python" for short, the same as the language) "thinks" there is something wrong with the statement you typed. But instead of reporting a syntax error, Python reports something else, which does not appear very helpful. (TypeError refers to the *type* of an object — an integer, a function, etc. — not to what you typed on the keyboard!) Apparently Python has decided that you were trying to call a function, named 2, with the input value 3+4, so Python tells you, in its own cryptic way, that 2 is not a function! You might think that Python can be really dumb sometimes. In fact, it is neither smart nor dumb — it's just a program.

Meanwhile, what you really meant was

```
>>> 2*(3+4)
```

Perhaps you thought that the multiplication sign was optional, like in math. Not so. Just as we warned you: every character matters!

Exercises

1.   Define *redundancy*.

2.   Type `2+-2` into the Python interpreter. Is this valid syntax? Explain the result. Now do the same for `2++2`.

3.■   Try `2+++2`. Explain the result. ✓

4.   Try `2**3` and `2**4`. What does Python's operator `**` do?

5.   In Python, pieces of text in single or double quotes represent *literal strings*. Try `"abc" + "def"` and `'abc' + 'def'`. Explain what the + operator does when applied to strings. ✓

6.   Can the `*` operator be applied to an integer and a string? Try `3 * '12'` and explain the result.

7.   Type in `9-8*2+6` and explain the result. Type in `(5-1)*(1+2)**3` and explain the result. What is the *precedence of operators* in Python expressions (that is, which operators are applied first)?

8.   Remove all redundant parentheses from the following Python expression: `(x - 2)**3 + (3*x)` ✓

9.   Suppose we have defined a Python function

```
def reciprocal(x):
    return 1/x
```

What is the result of

```
>>> 1 + reciprocal(2*5)
```

How is a Python expression evaluated when one of the operands is a function call? How is a Python function evaluated when the argument is an expression?

10.■   In Section 1.5, Question 1 you had a chance to experiment with Python's operator `%` applied to numbers. Determine its rank (precedence) as compared to `+`, `-`, `*`, `/`, and `**`.

2.4 Python Code Structure

Python wouldn't be much use if a programmer had to write every single statement separately. There must be a way to reuse a block of statements and execute this block multiple times. As we know, one way of doing this is to define a function. All programming languages let us define functions in one way or another.

Example 1

```
# This function calculates 1 + 2 + ... + n
#    using the formula sum = n(n+1)/2
def sum1ToN(n):
    'Returns 1 + 2 + ... + n'
    return n*(n+1)//2    # The // operator means
                         #    integer division
```

The above function, familiar from Chapter 1, calculates the sum of all positive integers from 1 to *n*, using the formula derived in that chapter:

$$1+2+...+n = \frac{n(n+1)}{2}$$

Once a function is defined, you can call it with various arguments:

```
>>> sum1ToN(3)
6
>>> sum1ToN(6)
21
>>> sum1ToN(100)
5050
```

In Python, the # symbol, unless it is within a literal string, indicates a *comment*. The purpose of comments is to make programs more readable for humans. A comment can document what a function does or explain obscure code. The interpreter does not care: it simply skips all the text from # to the end of the line (Figure 2-5).

```
# This function calculates 1 + 2 + ... + n
#    using the formula sum = n(n+1)/2
def sum1ToN(n):
    "Returns 1 + 2 + ... + n"
    return n*(n+1)//2     # The // operator means
                          #    integer division
```
Comments

Figure 2-5. Comments

`def` is one of Python's *reserved words* (also known as *keywords*) — words that have special meanings in a programming language. Python uses about 30 reserved words. `def` indicates that we are defining a function. `return` is another reserved word (see Figure 2-6). When you enter Python code in *IDLE* (the GUI front end), different syntactic elements are displayed in different colors. The reserved words are orange by default.

Reserved words

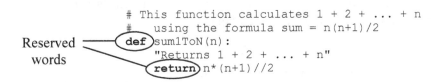

```
# This function calculates 1 + 2 + ... + n
#    using the formula sum = n(n+1)/2
def sum1ToN(n):
    "Returns 1 + 2 + ... + n"
    return n*(n+1)//2
```

Figure 2-6. Reserved words

Python is case-sensitive. All reserved words, except `True`, `False`, and `None`, must be written in lowercase letters.

Note the colon at the end of the "def" line — it is required by the syntax rules.

`sum1ToN` is the name we gave to our function, and `n` is the name we gave to its *argument* (input value).

It is essential to give meaningful names to functions.

A name in Python can consist of letters, digits, and underscore characters. A name cannot start with a digit. Python is case-sensitive, so `Sum` is different from `sum`. In our example, we could call our function `sumFrom1ToN` or `sum1_N`.

As you know, Python has several built-in functions with short names. These include `abs`, `id`, `input`, `max`, `min`, `pow`, `range`, `str`, `len`, and so on.

> **Avoid using these names for your functions: if you do, your function will override the built-in function, and you won't be able to call that function.**

The lines that follow the "def" line are *indented* to the right. The indented lines form a block of related statements, in this case the definition of a function. Indentation must be consistent within a block — this is one of the Python syntax rules. It is customary to indent the next level by 4 spaces.

> **When you write Python code in a text editor, use spaces rather than tabs for indenting lines.**

In addition to comments, it is customary to include a *documentation string* as the first line of a function, just below the `def` line (Figure 2-7). This string is optional. It is used to produce program documentation automatically.

```
# This function calculates 1 + 2 + ... + n
#    using the formula sum = n(n+1)/2
def sum1ToN(n):
    "Returns 1 + 2 + ... + n"  ──────────── Documentation
    return n*(n+1)//2  # The // operator means      string
                       #    integer division
```

Figure 2-7. Documentation string

❖   ❖   ❖

> **In Python, a simple statement is usually written on a separate line.**

One exception is literal strings enclosed within triple quotes `'''` or `"""`. Try:

```
>>> msg = '''And it always goes on
and on and on
and on and on'''
>>> msg
```

Python echoes the value of `msg`:

```
'And it always goes on\nand on and on\nand on and on'
```

\n in the message signifies the *newline* character. When encountered in the output text, \n shifts the next character position to the beginning of the next line. For example:

```
>>> print('And it always goes on\nand on and on\nand on and on')
And it always goes on
and on and on
and on and on
```

Or:

```
>>> print('Line 1\nLine 2')
Line 1
Line 2
```

Documentation strings often use the `"""` ... `"""` or `'''`...`'''` if they exceed one line.

If a statement is too long to fit on one line, you can put a backslash \ at the end of the line and continue on the next line. For example:

```
>>> 1 + 2 + 3 + 4 + 5 + 6 \
  + 7 + 8 + 9 + 10
55
```

However,

> **a preferred style of writing an expression on multiple lines is to put it in parentheses.**

For example:

```
>>> (1 + 2 + 3 + 4 + 5 + 6
  + 7 + 8 + 9 + 10)
55
```

Python lets you place several statements on one line, although this is not common style. To do that, you have to separate the statements with semicolons. For example:

```
>>> x = 3; y = 2; print(x + y)
5
```

Exercises

1.   The following function returns the first character of a string (or the first element of a list):

```
def first(s):
    return s[0]
```

Add a documentation string to this function and type all three lines at Python's prompt. Now try:

```
>>> first('Hello, world')
```

Then try

```
>>> first.__doc__
```

(Python uses two underscores on each side to mark special "system" names.)

2.   Identify three reserved words in the function shown in Figure 2-2 on page 25. ✓

3.   Identify two syntax errors in the following definition of a function:

```
def badCode(x)
    Return x**2 - 1
```

4.   What is the output from the following statement? ✓

```
print('One is better than \none' +\
    '; two is better than one')
```

5.   What is the output from the following statement?

```
print('Python is #1')
```

6.■   Find a syntax error in the following code: ✓

```
def mystery(n):
    'Returns n cubed'
    return n**3
```

7.▪ In Python, s[-1] refers to the <u>last</u> character of a string s (or the last element of a list s). Write a function that takes a string s and returns a new string that consists of two characters: the first and the last characters in s. Give your function a reasonable name. Include a documentation string in your code.

8.▪ Write a Python function triangle(s) that has only one print statement and prints

```
sssss
 sss
  s
```

where s is a one-character string. For example, triangle('*') should print

```
*****
 ***
  *
```

Can you omit the return statement in a function definition? If so, what will your function return?

2.5   Review

Terms introduced in this chapter:

CPU	*Programming language*
RAM	*Assembly Language*
Bit	*Syntax rules*
Byte	*Redundancy*
Kilobyte	*Parsing*
Megabyte	*Prompt*
Gigabyte	*Comment*
Gigahertz	*Indentation*
Compiler	*Reserved word* (*keyword*)
Interpreter	*Literal string*
Source code	*Function argument*
Debugging	

Some of the Python features introduced in this chapter:

```
def someFunction(x):
    ...
    ...
    return ...
```

A block of related statements is indented.
+, *, /, **, % operators
Literal strings: `'abc'`, `"abc"`, `'''abc'''`, or `"""abc"""`
\n stands for the newline character
\ at the end of the line means continue on the next line
marks a comment that extends to the end of the line.

3 Variables

3.1 Prologue

When we define a function using a formula, for instance $f(x) = x^2$, we might say something like this: for any real number x, let $y = f(x) = x^2$. x here is called a *variable*. Basically, it is a symbol, a name, used to represent any element of the domain of f. Think of a variable as a box with a name label on it. Some value is placed into the box named x and shipped to the processing plant f. The plant manufactures a new value, places it into a box named y, and ships it back to the customer. y is also a variable. Its value depends on x.

A similar concept is used in programming, only it is less abstract and more practical. In the theory of programming, a variable is a "named container" — basically a memory location with a nametag attached to it. Different values can be stored in the variable at different times. You can examine the value stored in a variable and place a new value into it.

3.2 Variables in Python

Example 1

```
>>> x = 3
>>> x
3
>>> x = 5
>>> x
5
```

In Python, every value is an *object*. Python supports several built-in types of objects: numbers, strings, lists, and so on. (A programmer can also define his own types of objects and create their *instances* in the program.) Python has a built-in function `type` that takes any object and returns its type.

Example 2

```
>>> x = 3
>>> type(x)
<class 'int'>

>>> x = 1.5
>>> type(x)
<class 'float'>

>>> x = 'Hello'
>>> type(x)
<class 'str'>

>>> x = '*'
>>> type(x)
<class 'str'>
```

What do we learn from these examples?

1. To introduce a new variable, all we have to do is give it a name and assign a value to it, using the *assignment operator* =.

2. If we enter the name of a variable, Python displays its current value.

3. Python has several built-in types of objects.

   • An object of the type `int` holds an integer value (in a certain range).

   • An object of the type `float` holds a real number (or its approximation). The type of a real number is called `float` because such numbers are stored in the computer as *floating-point* numbers. This is discussed in Chapter 5.

   • An object of the type `str` holds a string of characters (or a single character).

4. The same variable can hold different types of objects at different times.

5. Each object "knows" its own type. We do not have to tell the variable what type of object is stored in it.

Names of variables are chosen by the programmer.

> **A name of a variable can contain letters, digits, and underscore characters. A name cannot start with a digit. By convention, all names of variables start with a lowercase letter.**

As we said earlier, several built-in functions in Python have short, unremarkable names: `abs`, `bool`, `dict`, `dir`, `float`, `bin`, `hex`, `id`, `input`, `int`, `next`, `iter`, `len`, `list`, `map`, `max`, `min`, `oct`, `pow`, `range`, `set`, `str`, `bytes`, `sum`, `tuple`, and so on.

> **Avoid using the names of Python's built-in functions as names for your variables: if you do, your variable will override the function and you won't be able to call that function.**

`id`, `min`, `max`, `str`, `bytes`, `len`, `sum`, `pow`, `list`, and `next` might be especially tempting.

> **If you override a function name and then try to call it, you will get a "non-callable object" error.**

❖   ❖   ❖

Variables can be used in *expressions*.

Example 3

```
>>> taxRate = 0.05
>>> price = 48.00
>>> total = price * (1 + taxRate)
>>> total
50.400000000000006
```

How does the statement

```
total = price * (1 + taxRate)
```

work? First, Python makes sure that the variables `price` and `taxRate` have been defined. Then it takes their values and plugs them into the expression `price * (1 + taxRate)`. If one of the values is not compatible with the operation in which it is used, Python "raises an exception" (reports an error). If everything is OK, Python calculates the result and places it into the variable `total`.

 Note that the result is not exact. The error is due to the fact that real numbers are represented in the computer approximately, as binary floating-point numbers, and there may be a small error. There is a way to get a neater output:

```
>>> print('Total sale: {0:6.2f}'.format(total))
Total sale:   50.40
```

`{0:6.2f}` is a place holder in the format string, which right-justifies a `float` value in a field of width 6 with two digits after the decimal point; `0:` tells Python to plug in the first parameter (`total`) into the place holder and round it appropriately.

Once an expression is evaluated and assigned to a variable, its value does not change by itself, even if you change the values of variables used in it.

Example 4

```
# continued from Example 3
...
>>> price = 60.00
>>> total
50.400000000000006
```

To see the effect of the new price, you need to recalculate the expression explicitly:

```
>>> total = price * (1 + taxRate)
>>> total
63.0
```

A variable can actually be used to hold a constant. For example:

```
pi = 3.1415926535897931
```

(This constant is defined in the Python module `math`. You will learn later how to *import* it into a Python program)

To be honest, we haven't told you the whole truth about variables. In fact, Python variables do not hold objects — they hold *references* to objects. A reference is basically the object's address in memory. Some objects, such as long strings or lists, take a lot of space; it would be too slow to copy their values from one variable to another. Instead, when we assign b = a, we copy only the reference (that is, the address) from a into b. Both refer to the same object (Figure 3-1).

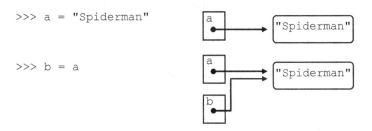

```
>>> a = "Spiderman"

>>> b = a
```

Figure 3-1. Python variables hold references to objects

This does not cause any confusion, as long as the object is *immutable*, that is, never changes. All numbers and strings are immutable objects: once created they cannot change. But lists, for example, are not immutable. Try this:

```
>>> a = [1, 2]    # list [1, 2] is assigned to variable a
>>> b = a
>>> b
...
>>> a.append(3)
>>> b
...
```

You have to be careful!

Exercises

1.   Define a variable *r* = 5. Define a constant for π. Define a variable called area and set it to the area of a circle of radius *r*.

2.   Explain the result of

```
>>> x = 5
>>> x = 2*x
>>> print(x)
```

3.▪   Which of the following are valid names for variables in Python?

     name, d7, 2x, `first_name`, `lastName`, `Amt`, `half-price`, `'Bob'`

     Which of them are in good style? ✓

4.   Define a variable `firstName`, equal to your first name. Define a variable `lastName` equal to your last name. Write an expression that concatenates (chains together) `firstName` and `lastName` with a space in between and assign that expression to a new variable.

5.   Can you predict the output from the following code?

```
a = 3
b = 2
a = a + b
b = a - b
print(a)
print(b)
```

6.   Can you predict or explain Python's responses to the following statements?

```
>>> age = 5
>>> print(age)
...
>>> print(len(age))
...
>>> age = 'five'
>>> print(age)
...
>>> print(len(age))
...
```

7.▪   Write a function `pow4(x)` that returns x^4 and performs only two multiplications. ✓

8.▪   What is the output from the following code?

```
n = 5
s = '+' * n
print(s)
print('len = ' + str(len(s)))
```

     ⸱ Hint: `str(x)` converts x into a string. ⸱

3.3 Scope of Variables

Suppose we have defined a function:

```
def distanceTraveled(t):
    '''Returns the distance (in meters) traveled in t
       seconds by a falling ball'''
    g = 9.8     # acceleration due to gravity in meters/sec^2
    return g*t*t/2
```

Test this function:

```
>>> print('{0:6.2f} meters'.format(distanceTraveled(1)))
  4.90 meters
>>> print('{0:6.2f} meters'.format(distanceTraveled(2)))
 19.60 meters
```

Now try:

```
>>> g = 10
>>> print('{0:6.2f} meters'.format(distanceTraveled(1)))
  4.90 meters
>>> print('{0:6.2f} meters'.format(distanceTraveled(2)))
 19.60 meters
```

The result returned by distanceTraveled has not changed, even though we have changed the value of g. Or have we? What is going on?

In Python and other programming languages, each variable is defined only within its *scope*. Scope refers to the space in the program's code where the variable is "visible."

A variable defined inside a function is called a *local variable*.

> **The scope of a <u>local</u> variable extends from the statement where it is first defined to the end of the function.**

A variable defined outside of any function is called a *global variable*. The scope of a global variable extends from the statement where it is first defined to the end of the program module (or until it is explicitly deleted with the `del` operator).

In the above example, we defined two different variables named `g`: a local variable within the function `distanceTraveled`, and a global variable. Within its scope, a local variable supersedes a global variable with the same name.

> **To avoid confusion, avoid giving the same name to a local and a global variable. Give longer, more prominent and meaningful names to global variables.**

It would be possible for a programming language to use only global variables. However, it would be very hard to keep track of where and how each variable was used: any function could change the value of any variable.

> **Python lets you use the value of a global variable within a function. But if you try to set the value of a global variable within a function, without an additional directive, Python would think that you were introducing a new local variable with the same name.**

> **Local variables in different functions can have the same name.**

In fact, it is good style to give the same name to local variables in different functions when those variables play similar roles in their functions (for example, `x`, `y` for coordinates, `r` for radius, `amt` for dollar amount, etc.).

Exercises

1.   Explain the difference between local and global variables.

2. In Python, the module called `math` has many math functions, including `sqrt(x)` for $\sqrt{x}$. To use it, you need to "import" `math` into your program (or into your interactive environment) by using the `import` statement

```
import math
```

The following function calculates $\dfrac{\sqrt{x}+1}{\sqrt{x}-1}$, and, in the process, it calls `sqrt(x)` twice:

```
def f(x):
    return (math.sqrt(x) + 1) / (math.sqrt(x) - 1)
```

Rewrite it to eliminate one of the calls to `math.sqrt`. ✓

3.♦ Explain why the following program does not work:

```
f=1
def factorial(n):
    k = 2
    while k <= n:
        f *= k        # same as: f = f * k
        k += 1        # same as: k = k + 1
    return f

factorial(5)
```

4. Compare the following two programs:

```
k = 10                    k = 10
def kTimes(x):            def kTimes(x):
    return k * x              k = 5
                             return k * x
kTimes(5)
                          kTimes(5)
```

Will either of them cause a syntax error? If not, what are their outputs?

3.4 More About Python Functions

The concept of a function in programming is broader than in math. First,

a function can have more than one argument.

Actually, mathematicians also consider functions of more than one variable. For example, $f(x, y) = \sqrt{x^2 + y^2}$. This is not a big deal, because several arguments can be viewed as <u>one</u> "tuple" (an ordered list of values).

Example 1

```
import math
def distance(x1, y1, x2, y2):
        return math.sqrt((x2-x1)*(x2-x1) + (y2-y1)*(y2-y1))

distance(0, 3, 4, 0)
```

The output is 5.0.

❖   ❖   ❖

A more interesting feature is that in Python

a function is not required to return a value.

Instead of calculating some value, a function can accomplish a certain task and not return a value. A function that does not return a value is more like a *procedure*. Some programming languages explicitly distinguish between functions and procedures. In Python we call everything a function.

Example 2

```
>>> def rotate(items):
        items.append(items.pop(0))

>>> numbers = [1, 2, 3, 4]
>>> numbers
[1, 2, 3, 4]
>>> rotate(numbers)
>>> numbers
[2, 3, 4, 1]
```

In Python, a function without a `return` statement returns the special default value `None`. Try:

```
>>> print(rotate(numbers))
None
```

❖ ❖ ❖

Furthermore,

> **a function (usually a procedure-like function) may take no arguments.**

Example 3

A Python function that takes no arguments:

```
>>> def print10Stars():
        print(10 * '*')

>>> print10Stars()
```

❖ ❖ ❖

> **Even when a function takes no arguments, you still need to put empty parentheses, both in the definition of the function and in the function call.**

Finally, a Python function can return different values for the same argument, depending on user input (and in some other special situations).

Example 4

```
def readInt():
    s = input('Enter an integer: ')
    return int(s)

print(readInt())
Enter an integer: 5
5
```

The function `readInt` prompts the user to enter an integer value and returns that value.

To summarize, a Python function may take several arguments, take no arguments at all, return `None`, or return different values depending on user input or other circumstances. As we can see, Python stretches the mathematical concept of a function beyond recognition.

Python also stretches the concept of the domain of a function. In Python, the domain of a function is basically the set of all objects for which the function works. If the function is called with an argument outside its domain, it *raises an exception*.

Example 5

```
def removeStar(s):
    "Removes the first occurrence of '*' from s"
    s.remove('*')
```

This function works for any "sequence" (for example, a list) that contains a `'*'` and has a *method* (*attribute*) called `remove`. For example:

```
>>> s = ['A','B','C','*','D']
>>> removeStar(s)
>>> s
['A', 'B', 'C', 'D']
```

However, the function `removeStar` *raises an exception* if we call it for a list that does not contain `'*'`:

```
>>> removeStar(['A','B','C','D'])
...
ValueError: list.remove(x): x not in list
```

Or for a string:

```
>>> removeStar('ABC*D')
...
AttributeError: 'str' object has no attribute 'remove'
```

❖   ❖   ❖

So, for all practical purposes, we can view a Python function simply as a fragment of code that is callable from other places in a program. A function may take inputs (arguments), perform a certain task or calculation, and return a value to the caller. Or it may raise an exception if the conditions for performing the task are not right.

Exercises

1.   Write a function that concatenates two given strings, with a space between them, and returns the new string. ✓

2.   Write a function `printHouse` that prints

```
  /\
 /__\
 |  |
 |__|
```

3.   Fill in the blank in the following function:

```
# Pads the given string s with spaces on the left to
# form a new string of total length w;
# returns the new string.
def rightJustify(s, w):
    'Returns s padded with spaces on the left'
    return _____
```

⟨ Hint: the built-in function `len(s)` returns the length of s. ⟩

Try

```
>>> rightJustify('123', 5)
>>> rightJustify(5, '123')
>>> rightJustify('123')
>>> rightJustify('12345', 3)
```

✓

4.   Type in the function `print10Stars` from Example 3 into the Python interpreter, then try

```
>>> print(print10Stars())
```

Explain the output. Define another function, `make10Stars`, that <u>returns</u> a string of ten stars. Explain the output of

```
>>> print(make10Stars())
```

5.   Consider the following function:

```
def printTriangle(n, ch):
    while n > 0:
        print(n * ch)
        n -= 1
    return 1
```

Try to predict the output from

```
>>> printTriangle(2, '*') + printTriangle(3, '#')
```

6.   Suppose we define the function `sum1toN` as follows:

```
def sum1ToN(n):
    if n > 0:
        return n*(n+1)//2
```

Try

```
>>> print(sum1ToN(6))
```

and

```
>>> print(sum1ToN(0))
```

Explain the results.

7.   Call the function `readInt` from Example 4, and when it prompts you to enter an integer, just press \<Enter\> (or type "asdfgh" and press \<Enter\>). Explain the result.

8.   Which of the following calls returns a result and which raises an exception? ✓

```
>>> len(0)
>>> len('0')
>>> len('''0''')
>>> len(''''''')
>>> len([0])
>>> len([])
>>> len((0))
>>> len(range(0))
```

3.5 Function Arguments

The variables that stand for input values in a definition of a function are called *formal parameters*, but people often just refer to them as arguments.

Example 1

```
import math

def distance(x1, y1, x2, y2):
    'Returns the distance between the points (x1, y1) and (x2, y2)'
    return math.sqrt((x2-x1)*(x2-x1) + (y2-y1)*(y2-y1))
```

x1, x2, y1, y2 are the formal parameters of the function distance.

To call this function we have to pass four arguments to it. For example:

```
>>> d = distance(0, 3, 4, 0)
```

❖ ❖ ❖

> **When a function is called, the number and order of arguments passed to it must match the number and order of the arguments that the function expects.**

Objects passed to the function as arguments are copied into the function's formal parameters.

More precisely, the references to (addresses of) the objects passed to the function are copied into the formal parameters.

Example 2

```
>>> def distance(x1, y1, x2, y2):
        return math.sqrt((x2-x1)*(x2-x1) + (y2-y1)*(y2-y1))
>>> a1=0
>>> b1=3
>>> a2=4
>>> b2=0
>>> distance(a1, b1, a2, b2)
5.0
```

❖   ❖   ❖

Within the function, formal parameters act as local variables. Their scope is the function's definition.

There is nothing wrong with reusing the names of the formal parameters as the names of the actual arguments passed to the function.

Example 3

```
>>> def distance(x1, y1, x2, y2):
        return math.sqrt((x2-x1)*(x2-x1) + (y2-y1)*(y2-y1))
>>> x1=0
>>> y1=3
>>> x2=4
>>> y2=0
>>> distance(x1, y1, x2, y2)
5.0
```

Python lets you supply default values for some of a function's arguments. The arguments with default values must appear at the end of the list in the `def` statement. For example:

```
def distance(x1, y1, x2 = 0, y2 = 0):
    'Returns the distance between the points (x1, y1) and (x2, y2)'
    return math.sqrt((x2-x1)*(x2-x1) + (y2-y1)*(y2-y1))
```

Now you can call `distance(x, y)`, and it will work the same as `distance(x, y, 0, 0)`.

❖   ❖   ❖

If you pass an immutable object to a function, the function cannot change it.

Example 4

```
>>> def niceTry(msg):
        msg += '***'

>>> msg = "You can't change me!"
>>> msg
"You can't change me!"
>>> niceTry(msg)
>>> msg
"You can't change me!"
```

The `msg` you changed inside the `niceTry` function is <u>not</u> the same as the global variable `msg` — `niceTry`'s `msg` is a <u>copy</u> of `msg`. So the statement `msg += '***'` creates a new string and places a reference to that string into the formal parameter `msg`, which acts like a local variable. That variable is never used: when the function is exited, the variable is destroyed. The global variable `msg` remains unchanged. To make it work as intended, the function should <u>return</u> the new string:

```
def appendStars(msg):
    return msg + '***'

>>> msg = 'Yes, you can change me'
>>> msg
'Yes, you can change me'
>>> msg = appendStars(msg)
>>> msg
'Yes, you can change me***'
```

Exercises

1. Define a function `mystery` that takes two arguments, `x` and `y`, and returns `x // y`. Call it for several pairs of integers, both positive, both negative, or one positive and one negative. What does Python's `//` operator do? Now call `mystery` with pairs of `float` values. How does the `//` operator work for `float`s?

2. Change `mystery` from the previous question to return `x / y`, rather than `x // y`, and retest it with pairs of integers. How does the division operator `/` work for integers?

3.   Write and test a function that takes two values, *a* and *b*, and returns their arithmetic mean, $\dfrac{a+b}{2}$. ✓

4.   What is the result of the following exchange?

```
>>> def swap(x, y):
        temp = x; x = y; y = temp
>>> a=1
>>> b=2
>>> swap(a, b)
>>> a
...
>>> b
...
```

Explain. ✓

5.   What is the result of the following exchange?

```
>>> def swap(pair):
        temp = pair[0]; pair[0] = pair[1]; pair[1] = temp
>>> pair = [1, 2]
>>> swap(pair)
>>> pair
...
```

Is a list an immutable object in Python?

6.   Explain why `pair` remains unchanged after the following exchange:

```
>>> def swap(pair):
        return [pair[1], pair[0]]
>>> pair = [1, 2]
>>> swap(pair)
[2, 1]
>>> pair
[1, 2]
```

7. Recall that the quadratic equation $ax^2 + bx + c = 0$ may have two roots:
    $x_1 = \dfrac{-b + \sqrt{b^2 - 4ac}}{2a}$ and $x_2 = \dfrac{-b - \sqrt{b^2 - 4ac}}{2a}$. Write and test a function
    that takes a, b, and c as arguments and returns a list of two values that are the
    values of the two roots. Avoid calculating $\sqrt{b^2 - 4ac}$ twice. Leave it to
    sqrt to raise an exception when $b^2 - 4ac < 0$. ⸮ Hint: don't forget to use

    ```
    from math import sqrt
    ```

    ⸮ ✓

8. Review the explanation of default values for function arguments at the
    bottom of page 52. What are Python's responses in the following exchange?

    ```
    >>> def double(x = 0):
            return 2 * x

    >>> double
    ...
    >>> double()
    ...
    ```

9.♦ The function below prints obj n times:

    ```
    def printNtimes(n, obj):
        'Prints obj n times'
        count = 0
        result = ''    # empty string
        while count < n:
            result += str(obj)
            count += 1
        print(result)
    ```

    Type in this definition and try

    ```
    >>> printNtimes(5)
    ```

    What happens? Change the function to print n stars ('*' characters) when
    the obj argument is not supplied.

3.6   Review

Terms introduced in this chapter:

Variable	*Local variable*
Expression	*Global variable*
Data type	*Function argument*
Floating-point numbers	*Formal parameter*
Reference to object	*Default argument*
Immutable objects	*To raise an exception*
Scope	

Some of the Python features introduced in this chapter:

```
x = value
def someFunction(x, y = dflt):
    ...
def someFunction():
    ...
someFunction()
None
```

4   Sequences, Sums, Iterations

4.1 Prologue

In math, a *sequence* is an infinite list of values. An element of a sequence is often called a *term*. We will deal only with numeric sequences — their terms are real numbers. The terms of a sequence are numbered by integers, starting from 1 or sometimes from 0:

$$a_1, a_2, ..., a_n, ...$$

or

$$b_0, b_1, ..., b_n, ...$$

The simplest sequence is the sequence of positive integers themselves: 1, 2, 3, 4, ... Another simple sequence is the sequence of positive odd integers: 1, 3, 5, 7, ...

Sometimes it is not obvious how a sequence is defined, given only its first few terms. For example: 1, 2, 5, 12, 27, ... It turns out we used the formula $a_n = 2^n - n$ to calculate the n-th term. So, it often helps to include the formula for the n-th term in the description of the sequence. For example: 1, 2, 5, ..., $2^n - n$, ... Or we can say simply: "Consider a sequence $\{a_n = 2^n - n\}$." The n-th term formula is called the *general term* of the sequence.

You can view a sequence of real numbers as a function whose domain is all positive integers (or all non-negative integers) and whose outputs are real numbers: $f(i) = a_i$. Like any other function, we can describe a sequence in words or with a formula. Sometimes, the only way to generate a long enough segment of a sequence is by using a computer. For example, the sequence of all prime numbers: 2, 3, 5, 7, 11.... . (An integer is called a prime if it is greater than 1 and is evenly divisible only by 1 and by itself.) In this sequence, we can find each term by looking for the smallest number not evenly divisible by any of the preceding terms. Another example: the sequence of all digits of π: 3, 1, 4, ...

There is a database of sequences of integers on the Internet, at `www.research.att.com/~njas/sequences/Seis.html`. It is called *The On-Line Encyclopedia of Integer Sequences*. The database contains over 100,000 "interesting" sequences (that is, sequences that came up in one mathematical problem or another). About 10,000 new interesting sequences arrive every year.

We say that a sequence *converges* to a certain number (called the *limit* of the sequence) if its terms get closer and closer to that number as n increases. For example, $a_n = \dfrac{1}{2^n}$ converges to 0; $a_n = \dfrac{(-1)^n}{2^n}$ also converges to 0. The sequence $1, -1, 1, -1, 1, ...$ bounces around zero but does not converge to any limit; $1, 2, 4, 8, 16, ...$ does not converge because its terms get bigger and bigger as n increases. When a sequence does not converge, we say that it *diverges*.

4.2 Arithmetic and Geometric Sequences

There are two types of sequences that come up frequently in mathematical problems: the *arithmetic sequence* and the *geometric sequence*.

> **In an arithmetic sequence, the difference between any two consecutive terms is the same.**

In other words, in an arithmetic sequence, $a_n = a_{n-1} + d$, where d is some constant. d is called the *common difference*. Thus an arithmetic sequence has the form $c, c + d, c + 2d, ..., c + (n-1)d, ...$. The general term of an arithmetic sequence can be written as $a_n = c + (n-1)d$. The simplest arithmetic sequence is, again, the sequence of all positive integers.

Example 1

$1, 3, 5, ..., 2n - 1, ...$ ($d = 2$) and $5, 15, 25, ..., 5 + 10(n-1), ...$ ($d = 10$) are both arithmetic sequences.

In a geometric sequence the ratio of the next term to the previous is constant.

In other words, in a geometric sequence, $a_n = a_{n-1} \cdot r$, so it has the form $c, cr, cr^2, ..., cr^{n-1}, ...$. The constant r is called the *common ratio*. The general term of a geometric sequence can be written as $a_n = cr^{n-1}$.

Example 2

1, 2, 4, 8, 16, ... and $\dfrac{1}{2}, \dfrac{1}{4}, \dfrac{1}{8}, \dfrac{1}{16}, ...$ are examples of geometric sequences.

❖   ❖   ❖

The concepts of arithmetic and geometric sequences are related to the concepts of the *arithmetic* and *geometric mean* (see Questions 7 and 8). The arithmetic mean (the average) of two numbers a and b is defined as $\dfrac{a+b}{2}$. The geometric mean of two positive numbers a and b is defined as $\sqrt{ab}$. Figure 4-1 gives a neat geometric interpretation of the arithmetic and geometric mean and demonstrates that the geometric mean never exceeds the arithmetic mean.

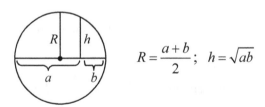

$$R = \frac{a+b}{2}; \quad h = \sqrt{ab}$$

Figure 4-1. Arithmetic and geometric mean

Exercises

1.   Come up with your own "interesting" sequence, defined in words. State its n-th term.

2.   Determine a formula for the general term of the sequence
$$\frac{1}{2}, \frac{1}{6}, \frac{1}{12}, \frac{1}{20}, \frac{1}{30}, \frac{1}{42}, \ldots . \checkmark$$

3.   Show that if $a_0, a_1, a_2, \ldots$ is an arithmetic sequence, then $a_0, a_3, a_6, a_9, \ldots$ is also an arithmetic sequence.

4.   Suppose the first term of an arithmetic sequence is 3 and the 7th term is 21. Find the 12th term. $\checkmark$

5.   What is the common ratio of the geometric sequence $4, 12, 36, \ldots$? What is its general term?

6.   Suppose the first term of a geometric sequence is 1 and the 11th term is 1024. Find the 21st term.

7.   Show that in an arithmetic sequence, each term (except the first) is the arithmetic mean of its left and right neighbors, that is, $a_n = \dfrac{a_{n-1} + a_{n+1}}{2}$.

8.   Show that in a geometric sequence with positive terms, each term (except the first) is the geometric mean of its left and right neighbors, that is,
$$a_n = \sqrt{a_{n-1} a_{n+1}} .$$

9.   Are there any sequences that are arithmetic and geometric at the same time? $\checkmark$

10.   What is the limit of the sequence $0, \dfrac{1}{2}, \dfrac{2}{3}, \dfrac{3}{4}, \dfrac{4}{5}, \ldots$? $\checkmark$

11.■   Does the sequence $\left\{ a_n = \dfrac{n-2}{n-5} \right\}$ converge? If so, what is the limit?

12.◆   What is the limit of the sequence $\left\{ a_n = \dfrac{n}{\sqrt{n^2 - 1}} \right\}$?

4.3 Sums

In many mathematical situations we are interested in the sum of the first n terms of a sequence. We have already seen in Chapter 1 that $1 + 2 + ... + n = \dfrac{n(n+1)}{2}$. A more interesting example is $1^3 + 2^3 + 3^3 + ... + n^3$. With a little algebraic technique it is fairly easy to show that this sum is equal to $\left(\dfrac{n(n+1)}{2}\right)^2$. In other words, $1^3 + 2^3 + 3^3 + ... + n^3 = \left(1 + 2 + 3 + ... + n\right)^2$. So it turns out that the sum of the first n cubes is always a perfect square.

❖   ❖   ❖

There is special "sigma" notation for sums: $a_1 + a_2 + ... + a_n$ is often written as $\displaystyle\sum_{i=1}^{n} a_i$.

Σ is the letter *sigma* of the Greek alphabet, written in the upper case. i is a *variable* — you can use j, k, or any other symbol. So we can write the sum of the first ten cubes as $\displaystyle\sum_{k=1}^{10} k^3$. The above identity that involves the sum of the first n cubes can be restated as $\displaystyle\sum_{k=1}^{n} k^3 = \left(\sum_{k=1}^{n} k\right)^2$.

Example 1

The sum of a geometric sequence

Let's start with a simple geometric sequence: $1, 2, 4, ..., 2^{n-1}, ...$. We want to find the sum of the first n terms of this sequence:

$$s_n = 1 + 2 + 4 + ... + 2^{n-1}$$

If we multiply both sides by *2*, we get:

$$2s_n = 2 + 4 + 8 + ... + 2^{n-1} + 2^n$$

— a very similar sum, with almost the same terms, except the first term is missing and 2^n is added on the right. If we subtract the first sum from the second, the same terms will cancel out, and we will be left with $2s_n - s_n = s_n = 2^n - 1$.

There is another way to prove that $1 + 2 + 4 + ... + 2^{n-1} = 2^n - 1$. We know that the formula works for $n = 0$: $1 = 1$. Let's assume that for any given *n*, the formula works for $n - 1$, that is $s_{n-1} = 2^{n-1} - 1$. Then

$$s_n = s_{n-1} + 2^{n-1} = \left(2^{n-1} - 1\right) + 2^{n-1} = 2 \cdot 2^{n-1} - 1 = 2^n - 1$$

so the formula works for *n*, too. From this we can conclude that the formula works for any $n \geq 1$. This method of proof is called *mathematical induction*; more on it in Chapter 11.

Exercises

1.   In Chapter 1, we showed that the sum $1 + 2 + ... + n$ is equal to $\dfrac{n(n+1)}{2}$, which is the average of the first and last terms, $\dfrac{1+n}{2}$, times the number of terms *n*. Show that the same is true for any arithmetic sequence.

2.   Derive the formula for the sum of the first *n* terms of the arithmetic sequence $\sum_{i=1}^{n} \left[a_1 + (i-1)d\right]$ in a different way, by reducing it to the known sum $1 + 2 + ... + (n-1)$. After simplification, your result should be the same as in Question 1. ≀ Hint: $\sum_{i=1}^{n} c = nc$; $\sum_{i=1}^{n} [(i-1)d] = d \sum_{i=1}^{n} (i-1)$. ≀

3.■   Find the sum of the the first *n* terms of the *telescopic* sequence $\dfrac{1}{1 \cdot 2} + \dfrac{1}{2 \cdot 3} + \dfrac{1}{3 \cdot 4} + ... + \dfrac{1}{n \cdot (n+1)}$. ≀ Hint: $\dfrac{1}{7 \cdot 8} = \dfrac{1}{7} - \dfrac{1}{8}$, for example. ≀ ✓

4. Show graphically that $\dfrac{1}{2}+\dfrac{1}{4}+...+\dfrac{1}{2^n}=1-\dfrac{1}{2^n}$. ∉ Hint: take a square pizza, 1 by 1 foot. Cut it in half. Cut one of the pieces in half. Cut one of the new pieces in half. Keep cutting... ∌

5.▪ Derive a formula for $s_n = c + cr + cr^2 + ... + cr^{n-1}$. Verify the result by applying it to the geometric sequence from Question 4. ∉ Hint: recall what we did with $1+2+4+...+2^n$ and use a similar method. ∌

6.▪ Find $\displaystyle\sum_{d=1}^{6} d \cdot 10^d$. ✓

7.▪ Find $\displaystyle\sum_{k=1}^{n}\left(2^k - k\right)$.

8.◆ Derive a formula for $1^2 + 2^2 + ... + n^2$. ∉ Hint: look for the formula in the form $An^3 + Bn^2 + Cn + D$; plug in $n=0$, $n=1$, $n=2$, $n=3$ to find A, B, C, and D. ∌

4.4 Infinite Sums

An infinite sum? Can $a_1 + a_2 + a_3 + ... + a_n + ...$ make any sense? Isn't such a "sum" always infinite? When you encounter infinity, it always raises infinitely many questions.

As it turns out, there is a way to give a precise mathematical meaning to an expression $a_1 + a_2 + a_3 + ... + a_n + ...$. Such an expression is called a *series*. The way to approach it is this: consider a sequence of sums s_1, s_2, ..., s_n, ..., where

$$s_1 = a_1$$
$$s_2 = a_1 + a_2$$
$$...$$
$$s_n = a_1 + ... + a_n$$
$$...$$

Here s_n is a normal finite sum, for any particular n. It is called a *partial sum* of the series.

> **If the sequence of partial sums converges to a number, that number is called the sum of the series. In that case, it is said that the series converges.**

You may still be not quite convinced: how can a sequence of partial sums ever converge? Aren't we adding more and more terms to the sum? But it is possible for the sums to converge if we add smaller and smaller amounts.

Example 1

For the geometric series $\dfrac{1}{2}+\dfrac{1}{4}+...+\dfrac{1}{2^n}+...$, $s_n=\dfrac{1}{2}+\dfrac{1}{4}+...+\dfrac{1}{2^n}=1-\dfrac{1}{2^n}$. As n increases, s_n approaches 1 (because $\dfrac{1}{2^n}$ approaches 0). The partial sums never quite reach 1, but they get closer and closer to 1 as n increases, and the sum of the whole series is said to be 1.

A series is often written in "sigma" notation, as follows: $\displaystyle\sum_{i=1}^{\infty} a_i$ or $\displaystyle\sum_{k=0}^{\infty} b_k$. ∞ is the symbol used for infinity. So $\displaystyle\sum_{i=1}^{\infty}\dfrac{1}{2^n}=1$.

> **For a series to converge, its terms must be getting smaller and smaller, converging to 0.**

Is the *converse* true? That is, if the terms of a series get smaller and smaller, approaching 0, then does the series necessarily converge? It turns out this is <u>not</u> true.

Example 2

The series $1 + \dfrac{1}{2} + \dfrac{1}{3} + \dfrac{1}{4} + ... + \dfrac{1}{n} + ...$ is called the *harmonic series*. Let us show that the harmonic series diverges. The idea is to split it into non-overlapping finite segments such that the sum of each segment exceeds a fixed number ($\dfrac{1}{2}$, for example). Here is the way to do it:

$$\frac{1}{2} = \frac{1}{2}$$

$$\frac{1}{3} + \frac{1}{4} > \frac{1}{4} + \frac{1}{4} = \frac{2}{4} = \frac{1}{2}$$

$$\frac{1}{5} + \frac{1}{6} + \frac{1}{7} + \frac{1}{8} > \frac{1}{8} + \frac{1}{8} + \frac{1}{8} + \frac{1}{8} = \frac{4}{8} = \frac{1}{2}$$

$$\frac{1}{9} + \frac{1}{10} + ... + \frac{1}{16} > \underbrace{\frac{1}{16} + \frac{1}{16} + ... + \frac{1}{16}}_{8 \text{ times}} = \frac{8}{16} = \frac{1}{2}$$

...

And so on. The segments get longer and longer, but we don't care: we have an infinite supply of terms to play with! So we can find a partial sum of this series that is greater than $\underbrace{\dfrac{1}{2} + \dfrac{1}{2} + ... + \dfrac{1}{2}}_{k \text{ times}}$, for any k, and therefore the harmonic series cannot converge.

Figure 4-2 shows an odd construction based on the harmonic series. The tower rests on one brick and extends to the right as far as we want without any other support! You can keep adding bricks at the bottom, with the displacement $\dfrac{1}{n}$. It is not very hard to show that the center of gravity of the top n bricks falls on the border of the $(n + 1)$-th brick.

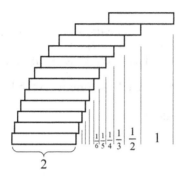

**Figure 4-2. A tower of bricks with one support can
extend horizontally as far as we want**

Example 3

The series $1+\dfrac{1}{4}+\dfrac{1}{9}+\dfrac{1}{16}+...+\dfrac{1}{n^2}+...$ converges. Moreover, its sum is a surprise:
$\dfrac{\pi^2}{6}$. It seems π pops up here out of the blue, but there is a deep mathematical
connection.

In general, the series is a fascinating topic that reveals many beautiful mathematical facts. Series are studied in Calculus, whose powerful methods help tell whether a particular series converges or not.

Exercises

1.   Find the sum of the *telescopic series* $\dfrac{1}{1\cdot 2}+\dfrac{1}{2\cdot 3}+\dfrac{1}{3\cdot 4}+...+\dfrac{1}{n\cdot (n+1)}+....$

       ⸘ Hint: see Question 3 in Section 4.3. ⸘

2.   Does the series $\displaystyle\sum_{n=1}^{\infty}\dfrac{n+1}{100n}$ converge? Explain. If yes, then what is its
       sum? ✓

3.   If $\{d_0, d_1, d_2,...\}$ is the sequence of digits of π, $\{3, 1, 4, ...\}$, does $\sum\limits_{n=0}^{\infty} \dfrac{d_n}{10^n}$ converge? If yes, what is the sum?

4.■   For which values of r does the geometric series $1 + r + r^2 + ...$ converge? ✓

5.   Does the series $1 + \dfrac{1}{3} + \dfrac{1}{5} + ... + \dfrac{1}{2n-1} + ...$ converge? Explain your reasoning.

6.■   Does the series $\sum\limits_{n=1}^{\infty} \dfrac{1}{n^3}$ converge? Explain your reasoning.

7.◆   The figure below illustrates the process or making a snowflake:

At each step, each straight line segment on the snowflake's perimeter is replaced by ⌐∧⌐ . If we keep repeating this process infinitely, we get a "curve" known as the *Koch Snowflake*. Suppose the perimeter of the first triangle is P and its area is A (where $A = \dfrac{P^2 \sqrt{3}}{36}$). Determine the perimeter and the area of the Koch snowflake after n iterations. Is the perimeter of the *Koch Snowflake* finite? What about the area?

4.5 Iterations in Python

In this section we will create a Python program that prompts the user to enter a positive integer nMax and prints out the sums $1 + 2 + ... + n$ for n from 1 to nMax. But first let us review what we have learned so far about Python's arithmetic operators.

Python supports int and float types of numbers. (It also supports the complex type, but we will leave this alone for now.) Python has +, -, *, and / operators. When +, -, and * are applied to two ints, the result is an int (as long as the result stays within the int range). If at least one of the operands is a float, the result is a float. The division operator /, when applied to two integers, gives a float.

Python has another division operator, //. When // is applied to two integers, a and b, the result is the largest integer that does not exceed $\dfrac{a}{b}$. For example, 15//2 gives 7, -15/2 gives -8.

For your convenience, Python also has the *augmented assignment* operators +=, -=, *=, and so on. a += b is the same as a = a + b; a -= b is the same as a = a - b, and so on.

Our program should print n and the sum $1 + 2 + ... + n$ for all n from 1 to a certain number nMax, entered by the user. Since we don't know ahead of time what nMax will be, we can't just write

```
print('{0:3d} {1:6g}'.format(1,  1))
print('{0:3d} {1:6g}'.format(2,  3))
print('{0:3d} {1:6g}'.format(3,  6))
print('{0:3d} {1:6g}'.format(4, 10))
...
```

It would also make little sense, since we would have to compute all the sums by hand. Even if we knew nMax, say nMax = 1000, and used a formula for the sum —

```
n = 1
print('{0:3d} {1:6g}'.format(n, n*(n+1)/2))
n = n+1
print('{0:3d} {1:6g}'.format(n, n*(n+1)/2))
n = n+1
print('{0:3d} {1:6g}'.format(n, n*(n+1)/2))
n = n+1
...
```

— our program would be too long.

Fortunately, Python provides an *iterative statement*, called a *while loop*, which allows us to <u>repeat</u> the same block of statements multiple times (but with different values of variables) while a certain condition holds true. The syntax for the `while` loop is:

```
while <condition>:
    ...
    ...
```

$<condition>$ is an expression that can use *relational operators* $<, >, <=, >=, ==$ (is equal), and $!=$ (is not equal). Its value is either `True` or `False`. Try it:

```
>>> 6 <= 6
True
>>> 5 <= 6
True
>>> 5 <= 4
False
```

$<condition>$ can also include *logical operators*: and, or, not. For example:

```
>>> x = 4
>>> x > 0 and x <= 3
False
>>> not x < 0
True
```

As long as the condition remains true, the program repeats the statements in the `while` block (the statements that are indented under `while`). Such repetitions are called *iterations*. Usually the condition includes a test for a variable that is updated on each iteration, so eventually the condition becomes false and the iterations stop. The program then continues with the first statement after the `while` block.

Example 1

```
nMax = 10
n = 1
while n <= nMax:
    print('{0:3d} {1:6g}'.format(n, n*(n+1)/2))
    n += 1
```

The output is:

```
 1      1
 2      3
 3      6
 4     10
 5     15
 6     21
 7     28
 8     36
 9     45
10     55
```

Thanks to iterations, the program code has the same length regardless of whether we run it with `nMax = 10` or `nMax = 10000`.

Example 2

Suppose we don't know the formula for the sum and want to use a "brute force" approach. We can calculate the sum $1 + 2 + \ldots + n$ using a loop:

```
sum1n = 0
i = 1
while i <= n:
    sum1n += i  # same as sum1n = sum1n + i
    i += 1
```

This loop can be *nested* within the first loop:

```
nMax = 10
n = 1
while n <= nMax:
    sum1n = 0
    i = 1
    while i <= n:
        sum1n += i
        i += 1
    print('{0:3d} {1:6d}'.format(n, sum1n))
    n += 1
```

Reminder: avoid using the names of built-in functions (such as `sum`, `min`, `max`, `int`, `str`, `bytes`, `len`, `pow`, `list`, and `file`) for your variables.

❖   ❖   ❖

Our programs are getting bigger, and it is no longer practical to test them in an interactive environment. It is much better to create a program with a text editor of some kind (for example, *Notepad*) and save it in a file. You can even use a word processor such as *MS Word* — just make sure you save the file as "text only." Or you can use an *IDE* (*Integrated Development Environment*).

It is customary to give Python *source files* (that is, files that hold the texts of Python programs) the extension `.py`.

IDLE, included with the Python release, provides a simple editor that allows you to enter and edit a program, save it in a file and conveniently run it. Let's try it. In IDLE, press Ctrl-N to open a new editor window (or use the menu command `File/New Window`). Type in the little program above and save it in a source file `Sums1toN.py` (Press `Ctrl-S` or use the menu command `File/Save`). Put the file in a folder of your choice, for example `C:\mywork`. Press `F5` to interpret and run the program. If you make changes to your program and press `F5` again, IDLE will prompt you to save the changed file.

You can have several editor windows open, and you can cut and paste text from one to another.

See `www.skylit.com/python/Appendix-A.html` for details and for instructions on how to run Python programs in other ways.

❖   ❖   ❖

Your program works, but it is inefficient: it keeps recalculating sums from scratch, over and over. If we have found $1 + 2 + ... + 49$, we only need to add 50 to it to get $1 + 2 + ... + 50$.

Example 3

We can keep track of the sum and eliminate the nested `while` loop, like this:

```
nMax = 10
n = 1
sum1n = 0
while n <= nMax:
    sum1n += n
    print('{0:3d} {1:6d}'.format(n, sum1n))
    n += 1
```

You might say: Who cares? Computers are fast anyway. However, such inefficiencies can visibly slow down even the fastest computer if the task is large enough. Here the version with nested loops will perform a number of operations proportional to nMax^2, while in the streamlined version, with one loop, the number of operations will be proportional to nMax — a big difference. In this case, the more efficient version also has shorter code.

We are almost done with our project. The only remaining question is: How do we get nMax from the user?

Python has a built-in function `input`, which lets you issue a prompt and read a string from the *standard input stream* `stdin`, that is, the keyboard.

Example 4

```
>>> word = input('Enter any word: ')
Enter any word: Hello
>>> word
'Hello'
```

`input` returns a string. We can convert it into an `int` by applying the built-in function `int`.

Example 5

```
>>> s = input('Enter a positive integer: ')
Enter a positive integer: 10
>>> nMax = int(s)
>>> nMax
10
```

❖ ❖ ❖

This works, as long as the user enters a string that represents a valid integer. But what if the user mistypes? For example:

```
>>> s = input('Enter a positive integer: ')
Enter a positive integer: 1.0
>>> nMax = int(s)
...
ValueError: invalid literal for int() with base 10: '1.0'
```

The program is aborted with a cryptic error message. In the technical Python lingo, the program *raises an exception* — in this case, a ValueError exception. This is not very friendly! We should really give the user another chance. Luckily, Python lets us convert the entered string into an int <u>tentatively</u> and "catch" the exception if it occurs.

Example 6

```
try:
    nMax = int(s)
except ValueError:
    print('Invalid input')
```

We will put this code inside a while loop to give the user as many tries as he wants:

```
nMax = -1
while nMax <= 0:
    s = input('Enter a positive integer: ')
    try:
        nMax = int(s)
    except ValueError:
        print('Invalid input')
```

We have initially set nMax to -1, so that the while loop executes the first time.

Look at the complete text of this program — it is in the Sums1toN.py file in the Py\Ch04 folder on the Student Disk.

We mentioned earlier that Python has a built-in function `sum`. To calculate $1+2+...+n$ we could simply write `sum(range(1, n+1))`. But it would be inefficient to use this call within a loop (the same problem as with nested loops). It would also have spoiled all our fun!

Exercises

1.   Modify the `Sums1toN.py` program to accept only an odd positive integer `nMax` from the user and print the sums of positive odd integers $1+3+...+n$ for $n = 1, 3, ...,$ `nMax`.

2.   Write a program that prompts the user for a positive integer n and prints all positive multiples of 6 (6, 12, 18, etc.) that do not exceed n.

3.   Using `Sums1toN.py` as a prototype, write a program that prompts the user to enter a positive integer `nMax` and displays n and $n!$ (*n-factorial*) for n from 1 to `nMax`. $n! = 1 \cdot 2 \cdot ... \cdot n$. ✓

4.■   Write a program that prints n, $s_1(n) = \sum_{k=1}^{n} k$, $s_2(n) = \sum_{k=1}^{n} k^2$, and $\dfrac{3s_2(n)}{s_1(n)}$ for

$n = 1, 2, 3, ..., 20$. Try to guess the general formula for $\sum_{k=1}^{n} k^2$ from the

resulting table.

5.■   Write a function `printSquare(n)` that displays a "square" whose side has n stars. For example, for $n = 5$, the output should be:

```
*****
*   *
*   *
*   *
*****
```

Use only one `while` loop. (Actually, in Python, you can write this function without any loops, on one line. Can you figure out how?) ✓

6. Write a function `myPow(x, n)` that returns x^n, where $x > 0$ and n is a non-negative integer. Do not use the `**` operator or the `math.pow` function — use one `while` loop. ⊰ Hint: $x^0 = 1$. ⊱ ✓

7.▪ Write a function `smallestDivisor` that takes an integer $n > 1$ and returns its smallest divisor that is greater than 1. For example: `smallestDivisor(15)` should return 3; `smallestDivisor(7)` should return 7. ⊰ Hint: `d` is <u>not</u> a divisor of `n` if and only if `n % d != 0`. ⊱

8.♦ A positive integer is called a *perfect number* if it is equal to the sum of all of its divisors, including 1 but excluding the number itself. For example, 6 = 1 + 2 + 3. Write a function `sumOfDivisors` that takes a positive integer *n* and returns the sum of all its divisors (excluding *n*). ⊰ Hint:

```
if n % d == 0:
    sumDivs += d
```

⊱

The smallest perfect number is 6. Write a program that finds and prints out the next perfect number.

9.♦ Using `Sums1toN.py` as a prototype, write a program that prompts the user to enter a positive integer `nMax` and displays the partial sums of the series $1 + \frac{1}{4} + \frac{1}{9} + \frac{1}{16} + ... + \frac{1}{n^2} + ...$ for *n* from 1 to `nMax`. For each *n*, display *n*, the corresponding sum, and $\sqrt{6 \cdot sum}$. Test your program with a wide range of user input including a non-number, a negative integer, and a valid positive integer.

⊰ Hints:

1. Don't forget `from math import sqrt`. After that you can call `sqrt(x)` — it returns $\sqrt{x}$.

2. The statement

   ```
   print('{0:3d} {1:8.6f} {2:8.6f}'.format(n, sum, p))
   ```

   will print all three numbers in an appropriate format.

⊱

4.6   Review

Terms and notation introduced in this chapter:

Sequence	*Series*	$\displaystyle\sum_{k=1}^{n} a_k$
Term (of a sequence)	*Partial sum*	
Converging sequence	*Converging series*	
Limit of a sequence	*Diverging series*	$\displaystyle\sum_{k=1}^{\infty} a_k$
Arithmetic sequence	*Augmented assignment*	
Geometric sequence	*operators*	
Sigma notation		

Some of the Python features introduced in this chapter:

```
from math import sqrt

+=, -=, *=, etc.

while <some condition is true>:
    ...
    ...

s = input('Enter ... ')

try:
    n = int(s)
except ValueError:
    print('Invalid input...')

print('n={0:3d} x={1:7.2g}'.format(n, x))
```

5 Number Systems

5.1 Prologue

What is 5, mathematically speaking? There are many possible answers. Five is how many fingers I have on my right hand. Five is what follows four. And five is the property that all sets of "five" objects have in common. But the last definition seems to be circular: How can we tell that two sets have the same number of elements without counting? And to count, you already need to know one, two, three, four, five...

It turns out, however, there is a simple method of comparing the numbers of elements in two sets without counting. If we can establish a correspondence between the two sets, such that each element of the first set is paired up with exactly one element of the second set and vice-versa, then we can be sure the two sets have the same number of elements. Suppose, for example, that there are several students and several backpacks on the playground. Ask each student to pick up one backpack. If there are not enough backpacks for all the students, the set of students has more elements, and if there are some backpacks left on the ground, the set of backpacks has more elements. If every student gets one backpack, and there are no backpacks left, then the number of students and the number of backpacks are the same. Another example: if you can touch with each finger of one hand a different object in a set, and no objects remain untouched, then the set has five elements.

It would be nice to create one special set of five different objects, so that we could compare every other set to it. Suppose the world is populated only by sets, as in pure set theory. How can we devise five different objects in such a world? Take the empty set $\varnothing$ — call it 0. Now take a set of one element: $\{\varnothing\}$ — call it 1. Now take the set that contains 0 and 1 as elements: $\{\varnothing, \{\varnothing\}\}$ — call it 2. $\{\varnothing, \{\varnothing\}, \{\varnothing, \{\varnothing\}\}\}$ is 3. And so on.

5.2 Positional Number Systems

Once we have figured out, more or less, what a number is, the question remains how to represent different numbers. What is 34, for example? This combination of two digits represents a crucial invention of human civilization, a *positional number system*. Without it we would still be writing 34 as XXXIV or something like that. Whereas in our system it is easy to see: 34 is three times ten plus 4. Ten is a magic number, the *base* of our positional system. We probably picked ten simply because humans have ten fingers. If you need to tell a stranger who doesn't speak your language that you are willing to swap your iPod for 34 apples, it is convenient to gesture three times with both hands open and then once more with four outstretched fingers. So the importance of ten is a human universal, constant across languages and cultures.

If you have a number $\underbrace{d_n...d_2d_1d_0}_{\text{decimal digits}}$, where d_i is the *i*-th digit, then that number is equal to $d_n \cdot 10^n + ... + d_2 \cdot 10^2 + d_1 \cdot 10 + d_0$. For example, $347 = 3 \cdot 10^2 + 4 \cdot 10 + 7$.

Now imagine what would happen if we humans had only three fingers. We would count 1, 2, ... and then what? Three would become our magic number! After 2 we would write 10, 11, 12, then 20, 21, 22, and then... 100. 21_3 (21 base 3) would mean $2 \cdot 3 + 1 = 7_{10}$ (7 base 10). 14 would become 112, and instead of 34 we would write 1021 ($1021_3 = 1 \cdot 3^3 + 0 \cdot 3^2 + 2 \cdot 3 + 1 = 34_{10}$).

The "base 3" system would have its advantages. For one, there would be fewer digits to learn, and it would be easier to learn how to count: one, two, ten, eleven, twelve, twenty, and so on. And you could live to celebrate your 100th birthday (our age 9), 1000th birthday (our age 27), and even 10000th birthday (our age 81). On the other hand, your phone number, instead of 10 digits, would need 20 or 21 — hard to remember.

We can do arithmetic on numbers written in base 3 (or any other base) in the same manner as we do arithmetic in base 10.

Example 1

Calculate $2211_3 + 102_3$

Solution

$$\begin{array}{r} 2211 \\ +102 \\ \hline 10020 \end{array}$$

1 + 2 (= 3_{10}) = 10_3 ⇒ write 0, carry 1.
1 + 0 + 1 (= 2_{10}) = 2_3 ⇒ write 2, carry 0.
2 + 1 + 0 (= 3_{10}) = 10_3 ⇒ write 0, carry 1.
2 + 0 + 1 (= 3_{10}) = 10_3 ⇒ write 0, carry 1.
Write 1.

Example 2

Calculate $2 \cdot 1423_5$

Solution

$$\begin{array}{r} 1423 \\ \times2 \\ \hline 3401 \end{array}$$

3 · 2 (= 6_{10}) = 11_5 ⇒ write 1, carry 1.
2 · 2 + 1 (= 5_{10}) = 10_5 ⇒ write 0, carry 1.
2 · 4 + 1 (= 9_{10}) = 14_5 ⇒ write 4, carry 1.
2 · 1 + 1 (= 3_{10}) = 3_5 ⇒ write 3.

Exercises

1. Find all two-digit numbers (base 10) such that the number is equal to twice the sum of its digits. Find all two-digit numbers such that the number is equal to 7 times the sum of its digits. ✓

2. Take any number and subtract from it the sum of all its digits (base 10). Show that that difference is always evenly divisible by 9.

3.▪   In a Sudoku puzzle you need to fill a 9 by 9 grid with numbers in such a way that each row, each column, and each of the nine 3 by 3 squares contains all the numbers from 1 to 9. Take any completed Sudoku grid and combine the first three columns into one column of 3-digit numbers. Do the same for the next three columns and the last three columns. Prove that the sum of the numbers in all three new columns is the same. What is the value of that sum?

4.   Write 15_{10} and 24_{10} in base 3. ✓

5.   Write 121_3 and 2020_3 in base 10.

6.   Write 10011100_2 in base 10. ✓

7.   Subtract 1 from 10000_3 and write the answer in base 3.

8.▪   Write 243_5 in base 7.

9.   Calculate $201_3 + 12_3$ and $201_3 - 12_3$ without converting the numbers into decimal representation. ✓

10.▪   How can you quickly tell whether a number, written in base 3, is even (that is, evenly divisible by 2)?

11.◆   Take a 3 by 3 magic square:

```
8 1 6
3 5 7
4 9 2
```

It contains all numbers from 1 to 9, and the sum of the numbers in each row, each column, and each of the two diagonals is the same. Subtract 1 from each number. Convert each number into a two-digit base-3 number (adding a leading zero where necessary). In the resulting grid, each row has 0, 1, 2 as first digits and as second digits, in some order. The same for columns. All nine combinations of two digits are different. Such an arrangement is known as *Greco-Roman square*. (The original design used the Greek letters α, β, γ instead of 0, 1, 2 as the first digits and the Latin letters *A*, *B*, *C* as second digits. Each row and each column would have all three Greek letters and all three Latin letters, and all nine combinations would be different.) Construct a 5 by 5 Greco-Roman square and then a 5 by 5 magic square.

5.3 The Binary, Octal, and Hexadecimal Systems

The next step, of course, is to pretend that we don't have any fingers at all, just two hands. Then we would have only two digits, 0 and 1. This base 2 system is called the *binary system*. In the binary system, non-negative integers are represented like this:

Base 10:	Binary:
0	0
1	1
2	10
3	11
4	100
5	101
6	110
7	111
8	1000
. . .	. . .

It is very convenient to use binary representation of numbers in computers: as we know, each bit in the computer memory can represent only two values, 0 and 1. However, binary numbers are hard to work with for humans because even small numbers are far too long in binary representation. For example, $98_{10} = 1100010_2$. We need a compromise: a system that is easy to convert to binary and also easy to read for humans (at least for programmers).

There are two such systems: *octal* and *hexadecimal*. The octal system uses base 8 and has eight digits: 0 - 7. Each of these digits can be represented by a three-digit binary number (with leading zeros):

0	000
1	001
2	010
3	011
4	100
5	101
6	110
7	111

To convert an octal number into binary, simply replace each octal digit with its 3-digit binary representation. Experienced programmers know the bit patterns for the octal digits and can translate them instantaneously.

Example 1

3561_8 = 011 101 110 001$_2$ = 011101110001$_2$

The reverse conversion, from binary to octal, is also easy: split the string of binary digits into triplets, starting from the rightmost digit (add leading zeros on the left if necessary), then write the corresponding octal digits.

Example 2

11010111100$_2$ = 011 010 111 100$_2$ = 3274$_8$

The hexadecimal system uses base 16. Its 16 digits are 0, 1, 2, 3, 4, 5, 6, 7, 8, 9, A, B, C, D, E, and F. A stands for 10, B for 11, etc.; F stands for 15. Each of these digits can be represented by a four-digit binary number, as follows:

0	0000
1	0001
2	0010
3	0011
4	0100
5	0101
6	0110
7	0111
8	1000
9	1001
A	1010
B	1011
C	1100
D	1101
E	1110
F	1111

To convert a "hex" (hexadecimal) number into binary, just replace each hex digit with its 4-digit binary representation. To convert back, split the string of binary digits into quads, starting from the right, and replace each quad with its hex equivalent. Again, experienced programmers remember the bit patterns for the hex digits and can do these conversions very quickly.

Example 3

```
B6F8₁₆ = 1011 0110 1111 1000₂

0111 0110 1110 1010₂ = 76EA₁₆
```

❖ ❖ ❖

These days, octal numbers are used less and less; the hex system is far more popular, simply because you can conveniently represent the value of one byte (eight bits) as two hex digits.

To convert a binary number into base 10 manually, it is faster to first convert it into hex, then hex into base 10.

Example 4

$$111010010_2 = \text{hex } 1D2 = 256 + 13 \cdot 16 + 2 = 466$$

❖ ❖ ❖

The same is true for converting decimal into binary: first convert the number into hex, then hex into binary.

Programming languages often support octal and hex constants. In Python, for example, a sequence of octal digits precedeed by 0o (zero and the letter 'o') represents a number base 8. Try it:

```
>>> 0o46 # octal digits
38
>>> -0o46
-38
```

A hex number is written with the `0x` prefix. You can use uppercase or lowercase letters for the hex digits:

```
>>> 0x1D2
466
>>> 0x1d2
466
```

In Python you can also use binary constants. A binary constant is written as the 0b prefix, followed by binary digits, for example, 0b100110.

Python has a way to convert a number into a string of hex, octal, or binary digits. Try:

```
>>> hex(466)
'0x1d2'
>>> '{0:x}'.format(466)
'1d2'
>>> '{0:04x}'.format(466)
'01d2'

>>> oct(38)
'0o46'
>>> print('{0:o}'.format(38))
46

>>> bin(38)
'0b100110'
```

You will often see hex numbers written with leading zeros, because hex numbers often represent the contents of a fixed-length group of bytes. In Python, an int value is usually represented in 4 bytes.

The built-in int function provides a way to convert a string of digits, written in any given base, into an int value. Try:

```
>>> x = int('46')    #default base 10
>>> x
46
>>> x = int('46', 8)
>>> x
38
>>> x = int('1d2', 16)
>>> x
466
>>> x = int('111010010', 2)
>>> x
466
```

As you can see, "binary" arithmetic is similar to regular arithmetic (Figure 5-1). To add two binary numbers, write them one underneath the other with the unit digits aligned. Add the unit digits. If the result is 2, subtract 2 and set the carry bit. Write the result. Add the 2s digits and the carry bit. If the result is 2 or 3, subtract 2 and set the carry bit. Write the result. And so on. Subtraction is similar.

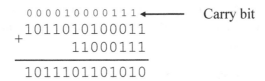

Carry bit

$$\begin{array}{r} 000010000111 \\ 1011010100011 \\ +\quad\quad\quad 11000111 \\ \hline 1011101101010 \end{array}$$

Figure 5-1.   Binary addition

Exercises

1.   What is the largest integer that has 7 binary digits? 15 digits? ✓

2.   Convert hex 90AB into binary.

3.   Convert binary 01011101011 into hex. ✓

4.   Convert hex F0C2 into octal.

5.   What are the results, written in base 2, of the following operations? ✓

1011100_2 * 4_{10} 1011100_2 / 4_{10}

6.■   Write and test a function that counts and returns the number of bits (binary digits) set to 1 in a positive integer:

```
def countBits(n):
    'Returns the count of bits set to 1 in a positive integer'
    . . .
```

For example, `countBits(12)` should return 2, because $12 = 0...01100_2$.

≶ Hints:

1. Check the digits from right to left.

2. n % 2 returns the rightmost (least significant) digit in the binary representation of n. (a % b is read "a modulo b," and means the remainder when a is divided by b.)

3. n //= 2 divides n by 2 and truncates the result to an integer, in effect shifting the binary digits to the right by one and getting rid of the least significant digit.

≷

7.♦ Write a program that prompts the user to enter a non-negative integer, converts it into a string of binary digits, and prints out the string. Pretend that the built-in function `bin` does not exist and implement the conversion in a separate function:

```
# Returns a string that represents a given non-negative
# integer n as a string of binary digits.
# Precondition: n is an int; n >= 0
def intToBin(n):
    '''Converts n >= 0 into a string of binary digits
    and returns that string'''
    ...
```

⟨ Hints:

1. You might want to get rid of the case `n == 0` right away:

```
if n == 0:
    return '0'
```

2. Go from right to left and append subsequent digits <u>at the front</u> of the result string:

```
s = str(lastDigit) + s
```

3. Convert the string of binary digits back into an `int` (using the `str` function) and print it out to test your `intToBin` function:

```
n = ...
s = intToBin(n)
print(int(s, 2))
```

4. Adapt the code from `Py\Ch04\Sums1toN.py` to prompt the user for a non-negative integer.

⋛

5.4 Representation of Numbers in Computers

In Python, `int` and `float` values are represented in a manner convenient for popular microprocessors.

An `int` usually takes 32 bits (4 bytes). If we used all 32 bits for representing unsigned (non-negative) integers in binary, we would be able to represent all the numbers in the range from 0 to 2^{32} - 1. Python interprets only the numbers in the range from 0 to 2^{31} - 1 as non-negative; for these numbers, the most significant bit is 0. The numbers in the range from 2^{31} to 2^{32} - 1 (that is, the numbers with the most significant bit set to 1) are interpreted as negative. The representation of negative numbers is called *two's complement*: unsigned n is interpreted as $n - 2^{32}$. In the two's complement system, `11....111` (thirty-two 1s) is –1; `11....110` is –2; and so on. The most significant bit becomes an indicator of sign (Figure 5-2).

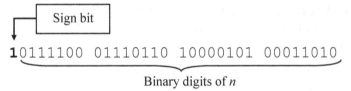

If the sign bit is 0, the number is interpreted as n (non-negative).
If the sign bit is 1, the number is interpreted as $n - 2^{32}$ (negative).

Figure 5-2. Representation of integers in 32 bits. Negative numbers are represented in two's complement system.

The two's complement system is convenient because $\left(2^{32} - x\right) + x = 2^{32}$, which is outside of the 32-bit range; the most significant bit gets lost, and the result is 0. The CPU can perform arithmetic as if operating on 32-bit unsigned numbers — it is not even aware of what we interpret as negative numbers.

> **In Python, `hex(-1)` returns `'-0x1'` and `0xffffffff` is converted into a positive integer. In other languages (C, Java) `-1` corresponds to `'0xffffffff'`.**

(In Chapter 7 you will write your own function that converts an `int` into a string of hex digits without the sign.)

A `float` usually takes 64 bits (8 bytes) and represents a number in the standard way expected by the CPU. Like scientific notation, this representation consists of a sign, a fractional part (*mantissa*) and an *exponent* part, but here both the mantissa and the exponent are represented as binary numbers. The IEEE (Institute of Electrical and Electronics Engineers) standard for an 8-byte (64-bit) representation uses 1 bit for the sign, 11 bits for the exponent and 52 bits for the mantissa. 1023 is added to the exponent to ensure that negative exponents are still represented by non-negative numbers.

This 8-byte format allows us to represent numbers in the range from approximately -1.8×10^{308} to 1.8×10^{308}, with about 17 decimal digits of precision. Note that you can represent in this format "only" 2^{64} different numbers, while there are infinitely many real numbers. Conversion from decimal to binary may introduce a small error.

There are many applets (little programs embedded into web pages) on the Internet that illustrate binary and hex representation of numbers and allow you to play with number conversions.

With a little work, we can also represent *rational numbers* in a computer. A rational number is a fraction with an integer numerator and denominator. As we said earlier, Python offers a way to introduce a new *class* of objects and redefine common operators for it. So we could define a class to represent fractions:

```
class Fraction(object):
    def __init__(self, num, denom):  # num is numerator
        self.num = num
        self.denom = denom
        reduce(self)
    def __str__(self):
        return '{0:d}/{1:d}'.format(self.num, self.denom)
    def __add__(self, other):
        return Fraction(self.num * other.denom +     \
                        other.num * self.denom, \
                        self.denom * other.denom)

    ... # etc. The code for the reduce function is not shown.
```

Then

```
>>> f1 = Fraction(1, 2)
>>> f2 = Fraction(1, 3)
>>> print('{0:s} + {1:s} = {2:s}'.format(f1, f2, f1 + f2))
```

would display

```
1/2 + 1/3 = 5/6
```

Exercises

1. If integers are represented in four bytes and negative numbers are represented in the two's complement system, what number does $FFFFFACE_{16}$ represent? ✓

2. Explain the result of

   ```
   >>> 1000000000.0 + 0.0000000001
   ```

3. Explain the result of

   ```
   >>> 3 * 0.1 == 0.3
   ```

4. Find the smallest positive integer n, such that in Python `int((17.0 / n) * n) != 17.0`. ✓

5. Python allows you to enter floating-point values in "calculator" notation, similar to scientific notation. For example, `1.23e5` represents 1.23×10^5; it will be displayed as `123000.0`. By default, Python also displays large `floats` in "calculator" notation. Find the smallest power of 10 and the largest power of 0.1 that will be displayed in this way.

6. Find the fraction with a denominator less than or equal to 20 that best approximates π.

     Hints:

1.
```
from math import pi
```

2. The built-in function `round` rounds a `float` to the nearest `int`; the built-in function `abs` returns the absolute value of a number.

3.
```
if distance < bestDistance:
        bestDistance = distance
        bestNum = num
        bestDenom = denom
```

5.5 Irrational Numbers

Between integers and fractions, all the numbers should be covered, right? That's what Pythagoras and his disciples believed, about 2500 years ago. Around 550 BC, Pythagoras founded a small religious "brotherhood," made up of Greek immigrants, in the city of Croton on the shores of southern Italy. Pythagoreans made great contributions to geometry, and they were the first to study numeric relations in music: they figured out simple ratios of frequencies for pleasant combinations of musical sounds. They literally worshiped numbers. But, as it often happens, their own discoveries eventually challenged their beliefs.

Pythagoreans believed that any number is either a whole number or a *rational number* (that is, a *ratio*, a fraction with an integer numerator and denominator). Pythagoreans thought of numbers in terms of geometry, as ratios of lengths of segments. They knew how to find the hypotenuse of a right triangle with the given legs (using the Pythagorean theorem, of course). So, eventually, they had to ask: what is the ratio of the diagonal of a square to its side? From the Pythagorean theorem, if the side is a, and the diagonal is d, we should have $a^2 + a^2 = d^2$ or $\frac{d^2}{a^2} = \left(\frac{d}{a}\right)^2 = 2$. So what kind of number is $\frac{d}{a}$? Is it a rational number? (The legend has it that when one of the disciples proved that this ratio cannot be a rational number, he didn't end well: fellow Pythagoreans drowned him in a fountain for this "heresy.")

The first proof of irrationality of $\sqrt{2}$ most likely used geometry. Something like this. Suppose the side of a square is mx and the diagonal is nx where m and n are integers and x is a "unit segment," a "common measure" of a and d. Let's assume that m and n are the smallest possible such integers. However, we can construct a smaller square (Figure 5-3) with the side $(n-m)x$, and the diagonal $(2m-n)x$ which has the same property: n-m and $2m$-n are integers. But these integers are smaller than m and n, respectively. So the initial hypothesis was wrong. This method of proof is called *proof by contradiction*.

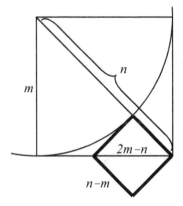

Figure 5-3. A geometric proof of irrationality of $\sqrt{2}$.

Here is a more modern, algebraic version of the proof. Suppose there exists a rational number $\dfrac{n}{m}$ such that $\dfrac{n^2}{m^2} = 2$. Let's take the smallest such numbers m and n (by reducing the fraction). $n^2 = 2m^2$, so n must be an even number. (If n were odd, n^2 would be odd, too.) So $n = 2k$, for some k. Then $n^2 = 4k^2 \Rightarrow 4k^2 = 2m^2 \Rightarrow 2k^2 = m^2$. So m must be even, too. Since both m and n are even, we can reduce the fraction further and get a smaller integer numerator and denominator. This contradicts the assumption that m and n exist in the first place.

That's how the first *irrational number* was discovered. $a + b\sqrt{2}$ (with integer a and b), $\sqrt{3}$, and so on are all irrational, too. Eventually mathematicians proved that π is irrational. Much later, in the 19th century, a German mathematician Georg Cantor proved that there are "significantly more" irrational numbers than rational numbers. Both sets are infinite, of course. Cantor devised a way to compare infinite sets. In his theory, the set of rational numbers is *countable*, that is, it belongs to the same category of infinity as the set of positive integers. The set of irrational numbers is in a different category of infinity: it is not countable.

Exercises

1. ■   Positive integers a, b, and c are said to form a *Pythagorean triple* if $a^2 + b^2 = c^2$. It is fairly easy to show that if we take any integers $0 < m < n$, then $a = n^2 - m^2$, $b = 2mn$, and $c = n^2 + m^2$ form a Pythagorean triple. For example, if we take $m = 1$, $n = 2$, we get $a = 3$, $b = 4$, $c = 5$. How many different pairs of integers $0 < m < n \leq 7$ are there? Write a Python program that will generate Pythagorean triples for all such pairs. ✓

    ⸮ Hint:

    Python supports objects called "tuples": a tuple is a list of items, separated by commas, within parentheses. A Python function can return a tuple. For example:

    ```
    return (3, 4, 5)
    ```

    You can print a tuple using the `print` function. For example:

    ```
    t = (3, 4, 5)
    print(t)
    ```

    ⸖

2.◆   If $a = \sqrt{2}$, then $a = \dfrac{2}{a}$. Let's start with $x = 1$ and repeatedly replace x with

the arithmetic mean of x and $\dfrac{2}{x}$. If we keep repeating this operation, x will

get closer and closer to $\sqrt{2}$. Write a program that uses this method to

evaluate $\sqrt{2}$ accurately to at least 5 digits after the decimal point. This

accuracy is achieved when $\left| x - \dfrac{2}{x} \right| < 0.00001$. Display the resulting estimate

and the number of iterations that was required to obtain it. Compare your
result with the value returned by `sqrt(2)`.

Hints:

1. `from math import sqrt`

2. `x = (x + 2 / x) / 2`

3. `abs(d)` returns the absolute value of `d`.

3.◆   The *golden ratio g* is defined by the proportion $\dfrac{g}{1} = \dfrac{1}{g-1}$, as shown in the

picture below:

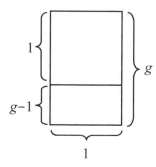

Solve the equation (see Question 7 in Section 3.5), then find the fraction with
a denominator under 50 that best approximates the golden ratio.

5.6   Review

Terms and notation introduced in this chapter:

Positional number system   *Floating-point number*
Base of a number system   *Rational number*
Binary system   *Irrational number*
Octal system   *Golden ratio*
Hexadecimal system
Two's complement representation
*   of negative integers*

Some of the Python features introduced in this chapter:

```
0x12AB, 0x12ab

0o123

0b100110

int('12AB', 16)

hex(466)

print('{0:04x}'.format(466))

from math import pi

from math import sqrt

t = (3, 4, 5); print(t)

abs(d)
```

6 Boolean Algebra

6.1 Prologue

A *proposition* is a statement that is either true or false. For example: "Henry likes macaroni," or "100 is a prime." Formal logic deals with the laws of reasoning that apply to propositions. Logical operations on propositions are not unlike arithmetic operations on numbers. In arithmetic, we can express common properties of operations using algebraic notation. For example, take the distributive law for multiplication:

$$a(b+c) = ab + ac$$

Similarly, we can use the notation of *Boolean algebra* to express general laws of logic. For example:

$$not\ (A\ and\ B)\ \Leftrightarrow\ (not\ A)\ or\ (not\ B)$$

$P \Leftrightarrow Q$ means "P is equivalent to Q" or "P is true if and only if Q is true." The above law says, for example: not (rich <u>and</u> famous) is true if and only if (not rich) <u>or</u> (not famous) is true. Formal logic is not very difficult: most of it is common sense.

There is a special notation for logical operations: $\neg$ means "not," $\wedge$ means "and," $\vee$ means "or." In this notation, the above formula would look like this:

$$\neg(P \wedge Q)\ \Leftrightarrow\ (\neg P) \vee (\neg Q)$$

However, we will continue using *and, or, not* for the sake of simplicity.

Boolean algebra is named after the British mathematician George Boole (1815-1864), who described the laws of logic in his books *The Mathematical Analysis of Logic* and *The Laws of Thought*.

6.2   Operations on Propositions

If you have two propositions, *P* and *Q*, the proposition "*P and Q*" is called their *conjunction*. For example, the conjunction of the propositions

> *I like coffee*
> *You like tea*

is the proposition

> *I like coffee <u>and</u> you like tea*

> **The proposition *P and Q* is true if and only if both *P* is true <u>and</u> *Q* is true.**

Conjunction (the *and* operation) can be described by the following table:

P	*Q*	*P and Q*
T	T	T
T	F	F
F	T	F
F	F	F

A table of this kind is called a *truth table*. It shows the values of a logical expression (here *P and Q*) for all possible combinations of values of variables.

"*P or Q*" is called the *disjunction* of *P, Q*.

For example, the disjunction of the propositions

> *He doesn't know*
> *He doesn't care*

is the proposition

> *He doesn't know <u>or</u> he doesn't care* (or both)

The proposition *P or Q* is true if and only if <u>at least one</u> of the propositions *P*, *Q* is true, that is, *P* is true <u>or</u> *Q* is true (or <u>both</u> are true).

Disjunction (the *or* operation) has the following truth table:

P	Q	P or Q
T	T	T
T	F	T
F	T	T
F	F	F

If *P* is a proposition, *"not P"* is called its *negation*. For example, "100 is not a prime" is the negation of "100 is a prime."

not P is true if and only if *P* is false.

Negation (the *not* operation) has the following truth table:

P	not P
T	F
F	T

In English, the words "and," "or," "not" can be used differently in different contexts. For example, a statement "Henry likes macaroni and cheese" most likely means that Henry likes macaroni <u>with</u> cheese, not that he likes macaroni and also likes cheese. In English, "or" is more often used as *exclusive or*: *P* or *Q*, but not both. For example: "Live free or die" means do one or the other, but not both. In Boolean algebra the operations *and*, *or*, and *not* have precise meanings, as described above.

Table 6-1 lists some of the important laws of logic. Note the *duality* of the laws: if you take a law of logic and replace each *and* with *or* and each *or* with *and*, you get another valid law of logic. (In Table 6-1, dual laws are written in the same block.) Of all the laws in the table, De Morgan's laws are the least obvious; these laws are very useful in computer programming. We gave an example of one in the prologue.

not (not P) $\Leftrightarrow$ P	Double negation law
P or (not P) $\Leftrightarrow$ T	Law of the excluded middle
P and (not P) $\Leftrightarrow$ F	Law of contradiction
P and Q $\Leftrightarrow$ Q and P P or Q $\Leftrightarrow$ Q or P	Commutative laws
P and (Q or R) $\Leftrightarrow$ (P and Q) or (P and R) P or (Q and R) $\Leftrightarrow$ (P or Q) and (P or R)	Distributive laws
not (P and Q) $\Leftrightarrow$ (not P) or (not Q) not (P or Q) $\Leftrightarrow$ (not P) and (not Q)	De Morgan's laws

Table 6-1. Some of the laws of formal logic

Exercises

1.   What is the negation of "I do"?

2.   What is the conjunction of "I did my homework" and "I went to see a movie"? ✓

3.   Rephrase in English the negation of "neither here nor there"? ✓

4.   Restate the proposition "I can't read or write" as a Boolean expression in terms of P and Q, where P is "I can read" and Q is "I can write." Write the negation of your expression and simplify it using De Morgan's laws.

5.   Make a truth table for the expression P or (not Q). ✓

6.■   Make a truth table for the expression P and (Q or R). ⸮ Hint: your table needs all possible combinations of T/F values for P, Q, and R, so it will have 8 rows. ⸮

7. Prove the De Morgan's law

not (P and Q) ⟺ (not P) or (not Q)

by showing that the truth tables for the left and right sides of this law are identical.

8. Write a logical expression with two variables, *P* and *Q*, that has the following truth table:

P	*Q*	?
T	T	F
T	F	T
F	T	T
F	F	F

⸎ Hint: write the expression as a disjunction of some of the conjunctions *P and Q, P and (not Q), (not P) and Q, (not P) and (not Q).* ⸎ ✓

6.3 Predicates and Sets

If *U* is a set, a function *p* with the domain *U* and the range {True, False} is called a *predicate*. In other words, a predicate is a function that returns either True or False. Suppose *p* is a predicate on *U*. Then we can consider a subset $A \subseteq U$ on which *p* is true:

$x \in A \iff p(x) = \text{True}$
(*x* is an element of *A* if and only if *p(x)* is true)

We will call *A* the *truth set* of *p* (Figure 6-1).

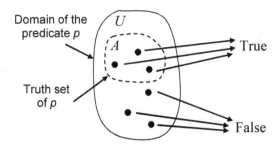

Figure 6-1. The truth set of a predicate

Example 1

Suppose U is the set of all real numbers: $U = \mathbb{R}$. The predicate p is defined as follows: $p(x)$ is true if $x \geq 1$; false otherwise. The truth set of p is the subset of all real numbers that are greater than or equal to 1: $A = \{x \geq 1\}$.

Example 2

U is a set of all integers: $U = \mathbb{Z}$. Describe a predicate that corresponds to the subset of all positive integers that are divisible by 3.

Solution

$$p(n) = \begin{cases} \text{True, if } n > 0 \text{ and } n \bmod 3 = 0 \ (n \text{ is divisible by 3}) \\ \text{False otherwise} \end{cases}$$

To define a predicate on U, we can simply specify a subset of U on which the predicate is true. There is a one-to-one correspondence between all the predicates on U and all the subsets of U. The predicate that is always true corresponds to the whole set U, and the predicate that is always false corresponds to the empty set.

If we have two predicates p and q, we can consider a new predicate: their conjunction, *p and q*. (*p and q*)(x) is true if and only if both $p(x)$ and $q(x)$ are true. The truth set of (*p and q*) is the *intersection* of the truth set of p and the truth set of q.

> The intersection of two sets *A* and *B* is the set of all the elements that belong to both *A* **and** *B*.

The intersection of *A* and *B* is denoted by $A \cap B$. The concept of the intersection of two sets is illustrated in Figure 6-2. Such diagrams are called *Venn diagrams*.

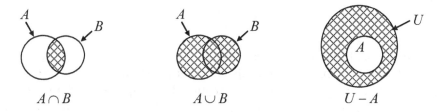

$$A \cap B \qquad A \cup B \qquad U - A$$

Figure 6-2. Venn diagrams for $A \cap B$, $A \cup B$, **and** $U - A$

Example 3

Let *U* be a set of all integers: $U = \mathbb{Z}$. Describe the predicate "*n* is a positive integer that is divisible by 3" as a conjunction of two predicates. Mark on the number line the truth set for each of them and the intersection of these sets.

Solution

"*n* greater than 0" and "*n* is divisible by 3."

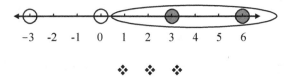

❖ ❖ ❖

If p and q are two predicates, we can consider a new predicate: their disjunction: *p or q*.   (*p or q*)(*x*) is true if and only if $p(x)$ or $q(x)$ or both are true. The truth set of (*p or q*) is the *union* of the truth set of *p* and the truth set of *q*. The union of two sets A and B is denoted by $A \cup B$ (Figure 6-2).

> **The union of two sets A and B is the set of all the elements that belong to A <u>or</u> B (or both).**

Finally, for any predicate *p* we can consider a new predicate, the negation of *p*, *not p*. If A is the truth set of *p*, then the truth set of its negation is $U - A$, that is all the elements of U that are <u>not</u> in A. $U - A$ is called the complement of A (in U). Once we agree on the "universal set" U, we can denote the complement of A in U simply as $\overline{A}$.

Example 4

Suppose we toss a coin three times and record the result as a sequence of three digits, using 0 for heads and 1 for tails. Let U be the set of all possible outcomes: $\{000, 001, 010, 011, 100, 101, 110, 111\}$. What is the truth set of the predicate "there were two tails in a row"? Now describe the negation of this predicate and its truth set.

Solution

The truth set of "there were two tails in a row" is $\{011, 110, 111\}$. The negation of "there were two tails in a row" is "there were not two tails in a row." Its truth set is $\{000, 001, 010, 100, 101\}$.

To summarize: every predicate *p* corresponds to its truth set A_p. Moreover, logical operations on predicates correspond to operations on sets:

Operation on predicates:	Formal notation:		Operation on sets:
p and q	$p \wedge q$	⟷	$A_p \cap A_q$ (the intersection of A_p and A_q)
p or q	$p \vee q$	⟷	$A_p \cup A_q$ (the union of A_p and A_q)
not p	$\neg p$	⟷	$\overline{A_p}$ (the complement of A_p)

Even the notation is similar: $\wedge$ and $\cap$, $\vee$ and $\cup$. This is an example of two mathematical theories that model each other. As a result, each law of Boolean algebra has a corresponding law in the algebra of sets, and vice-versa.

Example 5

One of the two De Morgan's laws is $\neg(P \wedge Q) \Leftrightarrow (\neg P) \vee (\neg Q)$. The corresponding law for sets is $\overline{A \cap B} = \overline{A} \cup \overline{B}$.

Exercises

1. Some students take drama. Some take chorus. Some take band. Some take two of the above. Some take all three. Draw a Venn diagram that illustrates this situation.

2. Sketch a set of all points x on the number line such that $(x-1)^2 \geq 4$. ✓

3. Sketch a set of all points (x, y) on the x-y plane such that $x \geq 0$, $y \geq 0$, and $x^2 + y^2 \leq 1$.

4. Sketch a set of all points (x, y) on the x-y plane such that $(x-2)(y-1) \geq 0$.

5. In a Sudoku puzzle, the objective is to fill a 9-by-9 grid with digits from 1 to 9 in such a way that each row, each column, and each of the nine 3-by-3 squares hold all the digits 1 through 9. The grid below shows a configuration of 1s and 2s on a Sudoku grid.

Mark all the remaining squares on the grid where both 1 and 2 are possible candidates.

6. In a study of health problems related to obesity, 32 percent of subjects were found to be obese, 14 percent had diabetes, and 9 percent both were obese and had diabetes. What percent of subjects were either obese or had diabetes (or both)? ✓

7.▪ Suppose two predicates p and q (on the same set) are such that if $p(x)$ is true then $q(x)$ is true. In this case we say that p *implies* q and write $p \rightarrow q$. Describe the relationship between the truth sets of such predicates. ✓

8.▪ Translate the laws of logic from Table 6-1 into the corresponding laws for sets.

9.▪ Prove the De Morgan's laws for sets using Venn diagrams.

6.4 `if-else` Statements in Python

Programs often need to decide how to proceed based on a certain condition. CPUs have special *conditional jump* instructions that either continue with the next instruction or jump to a different place in the program, depending on the result of the previous operation (see the example in Section 2.2). High-level languages have "if-else" statements for conditional branching.

Example 1

An `if-else` statement in Python

```
if len(s) > 0 and s[0] == '-':
    sign = -1
else:
    sign = 1
```

This statement works as follows: if s is not empty and the first character in s is `'-'`, then `sign` gets the value `-1`; otherwise `sign` gets the value `1`.

The general syntax for Python's `if-else` statement is

```
if <condition>:
    <statement 1A>
    <statement 1B>
    ...
else:
    <statement 2A>
    <statement 2B>
    ...
```

If the condition is true, the statements indented under `if` are executed; otherwise the statements indented under `else` are executed. After that, the program proceeds with the statement that follows `if-else`. Don't forget the colons!

The `else` clause is optional: you can have `if` alone. In that case, if the condition is true, the program executes the statements indented under `if`; otherwise, the program skips them.

Example 2

<u>`if` with no `else`</u>

```
if x < 0:
    x = -x
...
```

❖   ❖   ❖

If you want to "do nothing" under `if` and something under `else`, you can use Python's "do nothing" statement, `pass`.

Example 3

<u>`if` with `pass`</u>

```
if y == 0:
    pass    # do nothing
else:
    print(1/y)
...
```

❖   ❖   ❖

Often you need to chain several `if-else` statements together. For example:

```
def letterGrade(score):
    if score >= 90:
        return 'A'
    else:
        if score >= 80:
            return 'B'
        else:
            if score >= 70:
                return 'C'
            else:
                if score >= 60:
                    return 'D'
                else:
                    return 'F'
```

Python lets you simplify the indentation and compress the "else-if" on one line, using the keyword `elif`. The above code can be shortened to:

```
def letterGrade(score):
    if score >= 90:
        return 'A'
    elif score >= 80:
        return 'B'
    elif score >= 70:
        return 'C'
    elif score >= 60:
        return 'D'
    else:
        return 'F'
```

❖   ❖   ❖

Python has two special built-in constants: `True` and `False`. A condition is a Boolean expression that evaluates to `True` or `False`. So a condition is basically a predicate on the values of the variables involved. We have already encountered conditions when we talked about `while` loops, in Chapter 4.

Conditions are written using *relational operators* and *logical operators*. Python has the following relational operators:

Operator	Description
==	equal
!=	not equal
<	less than
<=	less than or equal to
>	greater than
>=	greater than or equal to

 The relational operators also apply to strings.

Python's logical operators, `and`, `or`, `not`, correspond to the logical operators of Boolean algebra. You can try these operators in the interpreter. For example:

```
>>> 3 >= 4
False
>>> 3 < 5 and 3 > 1
True
>>> 3 < 5 or 3 < 0
True
```

> **The relational operators take precedence over the logical operators: they are applied first.**

That is why we didn't use parentheses in the above examples.

Python has one more relational operator, `in`, which works with sequences (strings, lists, tuples, etc). `x in s` returns `True` if `x` is a character or a substring in the string `s`, or if `x` is an element in the list or tuple `s`. If `x` is not a member of `s`, `in` returns `False`. For example:

```
>>> 'a' in 'abc'
True
>>> 'b' in 'abc'
True
>>> 'bc' in 'abcd'
True
>>> 'cb' in 'abcd'
False
>>> 3 in [1,2,3]
True
>>> 2 in (1,2,3)
True
>>> [2,3] in [1,2,3]
False
```

The latter expression evaluates to `False` because the `in` operator does not work for "slices" of lists (sublists), only for single elements. `[2,3] in [1,[2,3]]` would give `True`.

You can also use the `not in` operator. `x not in s` is sometimes more readable than `not (x in s)`.

Example 4

Suppose `name` is a string and `guests` is a list. Write a code segment that checks whether `name` is in the list `guests`, and if so, prints "Welcome," followed by `name`. If `name` is not in `guests`, the code should print "May I help you?"

Solution

```
if name in guests:
    print('Welcome, ' + name)
else:
    print('May I help you?')
```

❖ ❖ ❖

Conditions can also include calls to Boolean functions. (By Boolean function, we just mean a function that can return only `True` or `False`.) Python has a small number of built-in Boolean functions, and you can write your own.

Example 5

The function `isPrime` below returns `True` if *n* is a prime number; otherwise it returns `False`.

```
def isPrime(n):
    'Returns True if n is a prime number; otherwise returns False'
    if n < 2:
        return False
    d = 2
    while d <= n//2:
        if n % d == 0:
            return False
        d += 1
    return True
```

```
>>> isPrime(5)
True
>>> isPrime(6)
False
>>> n = 7
>>> n < 10 and isPrime(n)
True
```

❖ ❖ ❖

You can return the value of a Boolean expression from a function.

Example 6

```
def greaterThan(a, b):
    if a > b:
        return True
    else:
        return False
```

is the same as:

```
def greaterThan(a, b):
    return a > b
```

There are commutative laws in logic: $P \wedge Q \Leftrightarrow Q \wedge P$ and $P \vee Q \Leftrightarrow Q \vee P$. With computers, things are slightly more complicated: you have to pay attention to the order of the operands. When a program evaluates a conditional expression, it actually performs certain operations. In the process it may encounter an error or raise an exception. For better efficiency and to allow more flexibility, many languages, including Python, use the *short-circuit evaluation* principle when evaluating Boolean expressions.

> **When evaluating** `p` `and` `q`**, Python first evaluates** `p`**. If** `p` **is false, the result is** `False`**, and** `q` **is not evaluated.**

> **When evaluating** `p` `or` `q`**, Python first evaluates** `p`**. If** `p` **is true, the result is** `True`**, and** `q` **is not evaluated.**

Short-circuit evaluation breaks the symmetry of commutative operations. For example, in

```
    if len(s) > 0 and s[0] == '-':
        sign = -1
    else:
        sign = 1
```

if s is an empty string, `len(s)` `==` 0, and the code will set `sign` to 1. But if we write

```
if s[0] == '-' and len(s) > 0:
    sign = -1
else:
    sign = 1
```

an empty string will raise a "string index out of range" exception, because the character `s[0]` does not exist.

Exercises

1.   Write a Boolean expression in Python that says "n is a positive integer and it is an even number." ✓

2.   Simplify using De Morgan's laws:

```
not (x >= -1 and x <= 1)
```

3.   Which of the following expressions are equivalent to
`not (a or (not b))`?

(a)   `(not a) or (not b)`
(b)   `(not a) or b`
(c)   `(not a) and b`

4.   Write a function that returns the number of days in a given month, specified by name: `'January'`, `'February'`, and so on. Use an `if-elif-else` sequence. ✓

5.■   Write a function `isLeapYear` that returns `True` if a given year is a leap year. (A year is a leap year if it is divisible by 4 but not by 100; however, if the year is divisible by 400, it is a leap year, too. For instance, 2000 and 2008 are leap years, but 1900 was not.)

6.   Using the function `isPrime` from Example 5, write a program that prints all the prime numbers under 1000.

7.   Write a Boolean expression in Python that is true if and only if the string s contains either a `'+'` or a `'-'`, but not both. ✓

8.▪ Fill in the blank:

```
# Returns True if ch is a hex digit '0' - '9', 'a' - 'f'
# or  'A' - 'F'; otherwise returns False.
def isHexDigit(ch):
    return _____
```

✓

9. For which values of x will the following statement raise an exception?

```
if x >= 0 and 1.0 / sqrt(x) < 0.01:
    pass
```

10.◆ Write a program that plays Rock-Paper-Scissors with the user and displays the cumulative score. For example:

```
Rock... Paper... Scissors... Shoot!
Make your move (r, p, s) or q (to quit): s

I said Rock
Ha! You are zapped -- 1:0

Rock... Paper... Scissors... Shoot!
Make your move (r, p, s) or q (to quit): p

I said Paper
Paper-aper! Tie -- 1:0

Rock... Paper... Scissors... Shoot!
Make your move (r, p, s) or q (to quit): q

Sorry, you lost! 1:0
Thanks for playing.
```

⸨ Hints:

1. The call `choice(s)` returns a randomly chosen character from the string s (or a randomly chosen element from the list or tuple s.). The function `choice` is in the module `random`, so you need

   ```
   from random import choice
   ```

2. Recall that `input(prompt)` prompts the user for input and returns the entered string.

11.▪   Write a function `isEarlierThan(date1, date2)` that takes two valid dates and returns `True` if `date1` is earlier than `date2` and false otherwise. Assume that a date is represented by a tuple `(month, day, year)`. ⟨ Hint: You can refer to the month, day, and year of the tuple `date` as `date[0], date[1], date[2]`. ⟩ ✓

12.◆   Suppose you already have a function `isPrime`, as shown in Example 5. Find on the Internet the definition of a *Mersenne prime* and write a function `isMersennePrime`. Do not duplicate the code from `isPrime` — just call it.

6.5   Review

Terms and notation introduced in this chapter:

Proposition	*De Morgan's laws*
Conjunction	*Predicate*
Disjunction	*Truth set*
Negation	*Intersection of sets*
Boolean algebra	*Union of sets*
"And" operation	*Complement set*
"Or" operation	*Venn diagram*
"Not" operation	*Relational operators*
Truth table	*Logical operators*

Some of the Python features introduced in this chapter:

`True, False` **constants**

```
if < some condition >:
    ...
else:
    ...

if < some condition >:
    pass
else:
    ...
```

```
if < condition >:
    ...
elif < other condition >:
    ...
...
else:
    ...
```

Operators ==, !=, <, <=, >, >=, in, not in
Operators and, or, not

```
return True
return False
return < Boolean expression >
```

7 Digital Circuits and
Bitwise Operators

7.1 Prologue

The circuit in Figure 7-1 shows a light controlled by an on-off switch: when the switch is closed, it turns on the light. If we put two switches in a row (Figure 7-2-a), both Switch 1 <u>and</u> Switch 2 must be closed to turn on the light. If we put the switches parallel to each other (Figure 7-2-b), Switch 1 <u>or</u> Switch 2 (or both) must be closed to turn on the light. Sounds familiar?

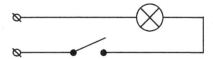

Figure 7-1. A circuit with a light controlled by one switch

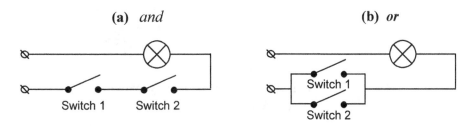

Figure 7-2. Arrangements of switches that model logical operations:
(a) *and* **(b)** *or*

The switches in Figure 7-2 are manual switches. A *relay switch* has an electrical magnet controlled by another current: when a current runs through the magnet, the magnet pulls in the lever that closes the switch (Figure 7-3). This way, one current can control another current.

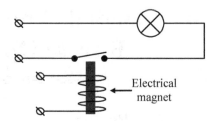

Figure 7-3. A relay switch

If you put two relay switches in a row, you will get an AND circuit (Figure 7-4-a). Two relay switches in parallel will make an OR circuit (Figure 7-4-b). You can also make a NOT circuit by using a special relay switch, which is normally closed, but opens when a current is applied to the magnet (Figure 7-5).

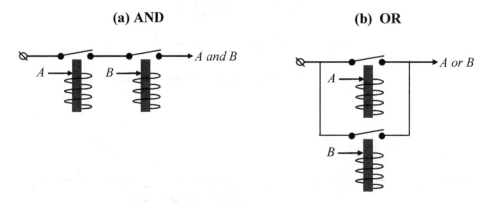

Figure 7-4. A circuit made of two relay switches:
(a) AND (b) OR

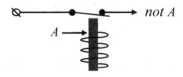

Figure 7-5. NOT circuit

AND, OR, and NOT circuits can be combined into more complex circuits. The output of one circuit serves as input to another.

In the late 1940s, John von Neumann, a great mathematician and one of the pioneers of computer technology, showed that any computation can be accomplished by combining AND, OR, and NOT circuits. So a computer can be built out of simple relay switches. In fact, some of the early computers were built that way (Figure 7-6).

Figure 7-6.   Harvard Mark II relay computer (1947)
Courtesy IEEE Annals of History of Computing

In modern *digital electronics*, microscopic transistors play the role of relay switches. Millions of transistors are etched into a small silicon chip. AND, OR, NOT, and other simple circuits are called *gates*. This type of circuitry is called *digital electronics* (as opposed to *analog electronics*), because only the presence or absence of a signal (electrical current) matters: "on" or "off," 0 or 1. The sizes (amplitudes) of the currents are the same — they are not used to carry information.

7.2 Gates

In diagrams of digital circuits, each type of gate is designated by a different shape (Figure 7-7). The table under each gate shows its output for all combinations of inputs. These tables are, of course, the same as the truth tables for the AND, OR, and NOT operations in Boolean algebra. Here 1 stands for True and 0 stands for False.

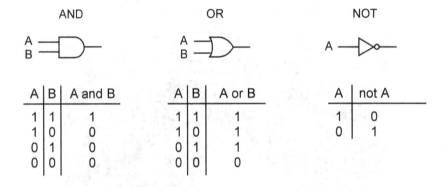

Figure 7-7. AND, OR, and NOT gates and their outputs

Gates are combined to produce more complex circuits.

Example 1

The circuit

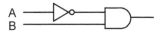

computes the logical expression (not A) and B. The output is defined by the following table:

A	B	(not A) and B
1	1	0
1	0	0
0	1	1
0	0	0

Example 2

The circuit

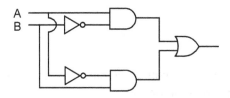

computes the logical expression

(A and (not B)) or ((not A) and B)

This is one of the ways to represent the *exclusive OR (XOR)* operation: the output is 1 if A is 1 and B is 0 or B is 1 and A is 0:

A	B	A xor B
1	1	0
1	0	1
0	1	1
0	0	0

Real digital circuitry uses more types of gates: simple combinations of AND, OR, and NOT gates are combined into "compound" gates as follows:

Gate name	Gate symbol	Is short for:
NAND		
NOR		
XOR		
XNOR		

Exercises

1. Draw an electrical circuit with three on-off switches, such that closing any one of them turns the light on. ✓

2.■ Suppose you have at your disposal several "two-way" switches. A two-way switch can toggle a wire between two other wires:

Design an electrical circuit that allows you to turn a light on and off from two different locations (for example, you can turn on the light from a switch at the door, then turn off the light from another switch by your bed, then turn the light on again from either switch).

3.▪   You have a battery-operated toy railroad and you want to be able to run a train forward and backward. The train's motor changes its direction of rotation if you switch the wires that go to the + and – contacts on the battery. You have a double two-way switch that can shift two wires from one pair of contacts to another:

Design a circuit that lets you reverse the direction of the train by flipping the switch. ✓

4.   Using only AND, OR, and NOT gates, draw a circuit with two inputs, *A* and *B*, that computes *A or (not (A or B))*.

5.   Which of the gates listed in this section has the following truth table? ✓

A	B	output
1	1	1
1	0	0
0	1	0
0	0	0

6.   Using only AND, OR, and NOT gates, design a circuit with the following truth table:

A	B	output
1	1	0
1	0	0
0	1	0
0	0	1

Propose two designs: one using one AND and two NOT gates, the other using just two gates.

7.   Using only AND, OR, and NOT gates, draw a circuit with three inputs, whose output is 1 if and only if all three inputs are 1. ✓

8.▪   The circuit in Example 2 implements the XOR operation. Design an equivalent XOR circuit (with the same truth table) using four gates: one OR gate, two AND gates, and one NOT gate.

9.■   Using only AND, OR, and NOT gates, design an XNOR circuit, with the following truth table:

A	B	output
1	1	1
1	0	0
0	1	0
0	0	1

Use no more than four gates total.

10.■   Using AND, OR, and NOT gates, draw a circuit with three inputs, whose output is 1 if and only if at least two inputs are 1.

11.◆   A "full adder" circuit has three inputs, A bit, B bit, and carry bit, and two outputs, the result bit and the new carry bit. Several adders can be strung together to perform addition on binary numbers:

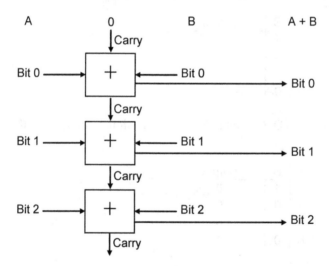

Design a full adder circuit using AND, OR, and NOT gates.

12.◆   Construct a "comparator" circuit with four inputs that represent two 2-bit unsigned binary numbers $A_1 A_0$ and $B_1 B_0$. The output should be 1 when the first number is greater than the second; otherwise it should be 0.

7.3   Bitwise Logical Operators

As we know, memory locations and CPU registers in a computer can hold binary numbers, combinations of 0s and 1s stored in individual bits. A typical CPU provides instructions that perform logical operations AND, OR, and NOT, on respective bits in the operands. (An operand can be one byte, two bytes, or four bytes.) A typical CPU also has the XOR instruction, which calculates the exclusive OR of the two operands. Figure 7-8 gives examples of the bitwise AND, OR, XOR, and NOT operations.

```
        01010110            01010110            01010110
AND  11110000        OR  11110000       XOR  11110000      NOT  01010110
     ========            ========            ========           ========
        01010000            11110110            10100110           10101001
```

Figure 7-8. Examples of bitwise AND, OR, XOR, and NOT operations

High-level languages usually provide bitwise logical operators that translate more or less directly into the respective CPU instructions. Python has the following bitwise logical operators:

Operator	Meaning
&	AND
|	OR
^	XOR
~	NOT

These operators work on `int` operands.

In Python, there is no direct way to enter a number in binary. You can use the `int` function to convert a string of 0s and 1s into an `int`:

```
>>> a = int('11001110', 2)
```

You can use your own function to convert a non-negative integer into a string of binary digits (see Question 7 in Section 5.3):

```
def intToBin(n):
    if n == 0:
        return '0'
    s = ''  # empty string
    while n > 0:
        s = str(n % 2) + s
        n //= 2
    return s
```

Try:

```
a = int('01010110', 2)
b = int('11110000', 2)
intToBin(a & b)
intToBin(a | b)
intToBin(a ^ b)
```

An alternative is to use octal or hex numbers. For example:

```
a = 0xCE
b = 0x0F
print('{0:02X}'.format(a & b))
print('{0:02X}'.format(a | b))
print('{0:02X}'.format(a ^ b))
```

The negation operator ~ is trickier. Because Python treats all integers as signed integers, ~a corresponds to a negative integer when a is positive. So you get

```
a = int('01010110', 2)
print('{0:02X}'.format(~a))
-57
```

> **Python does not give you an easy way to print out all the bits in a binary representation of a negative number.**

We know that an integer value is represented in four bytes, and that negative numbers are represented in two's complement form (see Chapter 5), but Python shields us from these details. In fact, there is no way in Python to represent 0x80000000 as a four-byte value: Python converts it into a positive value. So when working with bitwise operators, we will use only bits 0 to 30 of an int. We need to check the sign of a number to get hold of bit 31.

The & operator can be used to test whether a certain bit is set in a number, and the |
operator can be used to set a bit. The constants

```
0x0001, 0x0002, 0x0004, 0x0008, 0x0010, 0x0020, 0x0040, 0x0080
```

correspond to bit 0, 1, 2, 3, 4, 5, 6, 7, respectively.

Example 1

Test whether bit 2 is set in errorCode:

```
bit = 0x0004
if (bit & errorCode) != 0:
    ...  # do something
```

Example 2

When we say "set a bit," we mean "set the bit to 1." Set bit 4 in errorCode:

```
bit = 0x0010
errorCode |= bit  # the same as errorCode = errorCode | bit
```

The & operator can be also used to "cut out" certain bits from a number, that is to
leave only the values of these bits and set the remaining bits to 0s.

Example 3

Cut out the 4 least-significant bits from c. For example, if c has the value 0x482D,
then byte0 should get the value 0x000D.

Solution

```
mask = 0x000f
byte0 = c & mask
```

Example 4

Test whether bits 0-3 in `code` hold `1011`.

Solution

```
if (code & 0x0f) == 0x0b:
    ... # do something
```

Example 5

Test whether bits 0-7 in `pixels` are all set.

Solution

```
mask = 0xff
if (mask & pixels) == mask:
    ...
```

❖   ❖   ❖

In addition to bitwise logical instructions, CPUs have instructions that shift all the bits in an operand by a given number of positions. Python, too, has shift operators: << and >>. Try:

```
>>> a = int('11001110', 2)
>>> intToBin(a << 1)
...
>>> intToBin(a >> 3)
...
```

> **Shifting all the bits to the left by 1 is equivalent to multiplying the number by 2. Shifting all the bits to the right by 1 is equivalent to dividing the number by 2 (truncating the result to an integer).**

In other words, `a << 1` is the same as `a *= 2`, and `a >> 1` is the same as `a //= 2`.

Example 6

Write a function that returns the number of bits set to 1 in a given positive integer.

Solution

```
def countBits(n):
    count = 0
    while n > 0:
        if n & 0x01 != 0:
            count += 1
        n >>= 1
    return count
```

Or:

```
def countBits(n):
    count = 0
    bit = 0x40000000 # start with bit 30
    while bit != 0:
        if n & bit != 0:
            count += 1
        bit >>= 1     # in this version we shift bit, not n
    return count
```

❖   ❖   ❖

Exercises

1.   If a has binary digits `01100111` and b has binary digits `11010110`, write the
      result of `a & b`, `a | b`, `a ^ b`, `a << 1`, and `b >> 2`. ✓

2.   Evaluate `0xf8 & 0x8f`, `0xf8 | 0x8f`, and `0xf8 ^ 0x8f`.

3.   When a printer runs out of paper, bit 5 ("PE" — paper end) and bit 3
      ("ERROR") in the 8-bit printer status register are both set to 1. Write a code
      fragment that tests whether the value `statusReg` indicates that the printer is
      out of paper. ✓

4.   Fill in the blank in the following function without using the % operator:

```
# Returns True if n is divisible by 8;
# otherwise returns false
def divisibleBy8(n):
    return _____
```

5.   Write a statement that replaces bits 0-23 of pattern with their negatives, that is, replaces all 0s with 1s and 1s with 0s in those bits. Bits 24-31 of pattern should remain unchanged. ✓

6.   If a is equal to 0x00C5, what are the hex digits of a | (a >> 1)?

7.   Write a Python statement that tests whether any of the bits 1, 3, or 5 is set in byte. ✓

8.▪   Write a function that takes a given int and returns a string of 0s and 1s that correspond to the 32 bits of the number. Make sure your function works for both positive and negative values (and, of course, for 0, too). ∈ Hints: use Example 6 as a prototype; see also Question 7 in Section 5.3; use the sign of the number to test bit 31. ∋

9.▪   Write a function that returns the string of 8 hex digits in an int value. Make sure your function works for both positive and negative values; it should treat negative values as unsigned 32-bit binary numbers.

  ∈ Hints:

  1. Cut out the four least significant bits from the number, then shift the number to the right by four; repeat 8 times. (When you shift a negative number, the sign bit shifts, too, and the bits to the left of the sign are filled with 1s.)

  2. Use hexDigits[d] to get a hex digit that corresponds to d, where $0 \leq d \leq 15$ and hexDigits='0123456789abcdef'.
     ∋ ✓

10.▪   Write and test a Python function that takes an int value and returns a new int with bits 0-29 in reverse order. Bits 30-31 are assumed to be 0 and remain unchanged. ✓

11. A tic-tac-toe position is represented in 27 bits (bits 0-26), three bits for each square. 000 means an empty square, 001 means an X, and 010 means an O. The triplets of bits go in order left to right; first the top row, then the middle row, then the bottom row. The top left square is in bits 24-26; the bottom right corner is in bits 0-2. For example,

is represented as

$$0 0 0 0 1 0 0 0 0 0 0 0 0 1 0 0 0 0 0 1 0 0 1 0 1 0$$

Write a code fragment that checks whether there is an X in the central square. ⁊ Hint: it is more convenient to use octal representation of numbers. ⁊

12. Write a function that tests whether a tic-tac-toe position, as described in Question 11, has a win (three in a row, including diagonals) for X's.

13. Find out whether the & and | operators can be applied to Boolean expressions and, if so, whether they use short-circuit evaluation.

14. Explain the results of

```
>>> ~True
```

and

```
>>> ~False
```

15.♦ Bits 0-23 in a positive integer represent a line of pixels (picture elements) in a black and white image (the remaining bits are 0s). 1 stands for black and 0 stands for white. We want to fill all single-pixel holes in the line, so that each pixel with black left and right neighbors becomes black. For example,

```
011110111000011011010000
```

should become

```
011111111000011111110000
```

Fill in the blank in the following function that does this and returns an `int` corresponding to the new line of pixels (with bits 0-23 updated as necessary and bits 24-31 set to 0).

```
def fillHoles(n):
    return _____
```

16.■ Write a Boolean expression that evaluates to `True` if and only if the binary representation of n does not have two 1s in a row (assuming $0 \le n < 2^{16}$).

7.4   Review

Terms introduced in this chapter:

> *Digital circuit*
> *AND, OR, and NOT gates*
> *XOR (exclusive OR)*
> *Bitwise logical operators*
> *Shift operators*

Some of the Python features introduced in this chapter:

> &, |, ^, and ~ operators

> >> and << operators

8 Counting

8.1 Prologue

Combinatorics is a branch of mathematics that deals with counting all possible combinations, arrangements, sequences, or sets of objects. For example: Ice cream comes in two sizes, three flavors, and with any one of five toppings; in how many different ways can you order an ice cream? It is often not feasible simply to list and count all possible arrangements or combinations; combinatorics offers more sophisticated methods of counting. These methods are not very complicated: they basically use the four arithmetic operations. The trick is to know when to multiply, when to divide, when to add, and when to subtract.

Counting methods came to prominence in the 17th century when Blaise Pascal (1623-1662) and others got interested in computing the odds in gambling games. For example, what are the odds of getting 11 when we roll two dice? To find out, we need to know the number of all favorable outcomes (possible rolls that give 11) and the number of all possible outcomes. Using combinatorial counting techniques, we can analyze the likelihood of different arrangements and outcomes in card games such as Poker and Blackjack, dice games such as Craps, and so on. We can also analyze the complexity of computer algorithms and the running time and required space for computer programs.

8.2 The Multiplication Rule

The key operation in combinatorics is multiplication.

> **Suppose an object is described by two independent attributes. The total number of possible combinations of their values is equal to the number of possible values for the first attribute <u>times</u> the number of possible values for the second attribute.**

The multiplication rule is illustrated in Figure 8-1.

**Figure 8-1. 3 shapes of the mouth and 2 colors make
6 possible faces.**

If an object has three, four, or *k* attributes, then we multiply three, four, or *k* numbers, respectively.

Example 1

How many two-digit positive integers are there?

Solution

We can choose the tens digit in 9 ways (1 through 9) and the units digit in 10 ways. The answer is $9 \cdot 10 = 90$.

Example 2

A license plate has three digits followed by three letters. All combinations of digits and letters are allowed. What is the total number of possible license plates?

Solution

There are 10 ways to choose the first digit, 10 for the second digit, and 10 for the third digit. There are 26 ways to choose the first letter; same for the second letter and the third letter. The answer is $10 \cdot 10 \cdot 10 \cdot 26 \cdot 26 \cdot 26 = 17{,}576{,}000$.

Example 3

How many different values can be represented in one byte?

Solution

There are 2 ways to set the first bit, 2 ways to set the second bit, and so on. The answer is $2^8 = 256$.

❖   ❖   ❖

The multiplication rule explains how very large numbers can easily arise in combinatorial problems — or why it is so hard to win the lottery.

Example 4

How many ways are there to cover a whole 19 by 19 Go board with white and black stones?

Solution

2^{361} — more than 2×10^{120}, that is many times more than there are atoms in the universe.

Exercises

1. A combination lock has three wheels with the digits 0 through 9 on each wheel. What is the total number of possible combinations? ✓

2. Ice cream comes in two sizes, three flavors, and with any one of five toppings. In how many different ways can you order an ice cream?

3. How many three-letter names are possible in Python, such that all letters are in lower case, the middle letter is a vowel ('a', 'e', 'i', 'o', 'u') and the other two are consonants? ✓

4. An experiment consists of tossing a coin 10 times. The outcome is recorded as a string of ten letters, either "H" or "T". How many different outcome strings are possible?

5.■ In how many ways can we split 10 different marbles between two kids?
   ⸢ Hint: see Question 4. ⸣

6.■   What is the number of all possible subsets of a set of ten elements, including the empty set and the whole set? ⸘ Hint: see Question 5. ⸘

7.   What is the number of all possible colors that can be shown on a computer screen, if the graphics adapter generates a color using 16 bits for each of the red, green, and blue components of the color? ✓

8.■   What is the number of all possible configurations of five disks of different sizes on three pegs if we are not allowed to place a bigger disk on top of a smaller one?

8.3   Permutations

The multiplication rule also applies when we want to count possible arrangements of objects without repetition.

Example 1

In how many ways can a coach choose three players, a point guard, a shooting guard, and a center, from a team of seven players?

Solution

If they came from three different teams, we could choose the first player in 7 ways, the second player in 7 ways, and the third player in 7 ways. But here we cannot just multiply $7 \cdot 7 \cdot 7$ because all three players come from the same team. Once we have chosen the first player, there are only 6 players left. So we can choose the second player in 6 different ways. Once we have done that, there are only 5 players left, so we can choose the third player in 5 different ways. The answer is $7 \cdot 6 \cdot 5$.

Example 2

How many ways are there to seat 6 students in a classroom with 20 desks?

Solution

We can seat the first student at any one of the 20 desks, the second student at any one of the remaining 19 desks, and so on. The answer is $20 \cdot 19 \cdot 18 \cdot 17 \cdot 16 \cdot 15 = 27,907,200$.

> **An ordering of *n* different objects or symbols is called a *permutation*.**
> **There are $n \cdot (n-1) \cdot ... \cdot 2 \cdot 1 = n!$ possible permutations of *n* objects.**

We can choose the object for the first position in *n* ways, for the second position in $n-1$ ways, and so on. Only one object remains for the last position.

> **Recall that the product $1 \cdot 2 \cdot ... \cdot n = n \cdot (n-1) \cdot ... \cdot 1$ is called**
> **"*n*-factorial." It is denoted by *n*!.**

It is possible to arrive at the above result in a different way. Let P_n be the number of permutations of *n* objects. Let's take *n* objects, call one of them *x* and set it aside. There are P_{n-1} permutations of the remaining $n-1$ objects. For each of these P_{n-1} permutations, we can insert *x* at the beginning, between any two objects, or at the end, thus creating *n* different permutations of *n* objects. So, from each of the P_{n-1} permutations of $n-1$ objects, we now obtained *n* different permutations of *n* objects. Therefore, $P_n = nP_{n-1}$. Also, $P_1 = 1$, because there is only one permutation of 1 object. It is now clear that $P_n = n!$. To complete the proof more formally we would need to refer to *mathematical induction*, which is explained in Chapter 11.

Example 3

How many ways are there to put 5 different party hats on 5 people?

Solution

$5! = 120$.

Example 4

How many ways are there to arrange the cards in the deck of 52 cards?

Solution

$52! = 80658175170943878571660636856403766975289505440883277824000000000000$.

Exercises

1. How many three-digit integers have all different digits? ✓

2.▪ How many five-letter "words" (strings of letters) do not have the same letter twice in a row? Count any combination of letters as a "word."

3. How many ways are there to choose "most likely to succeed," "best athlete," "best dancer," "best dressed," and "class clown," a boy and a girl in each category, in a graduating middle school class of 30 girls and 36 boys? The same person cannot be chosen in two categories. ✓

4. How many ways are there to seat 6 people in a row of 8 chairs? ✓

5.▪ How many ways are there to seat 8 people in a row of 6 chairs, with two people left out? ⋞ Hint: assign chairs to people, not people to chairs. ⋟ ✓

6. How many pages will be required to print all possible permutations of letters "ABCDEFGHIJKL"? Each permutation is printed on a separate line; 60 lines fit on a page.

7.▪ Amelia is solving the cryptarithmetic puzzle

```
   S E N D
 + M O R E
 ---------
 M O N E Y
```

Her method is to try all possible substitutions of different digits for different letters (excluding 0 for 'M' and 'S', because a number cannot start with a 0). If she takes one minute for each try (her addition skills are excellent) and finds the answer after trying half of all possible substitutions, how long will it take Amelia to solve the puzzle? ✓

8.**■**   Two words are called *anagrams* of each other if they are made up of the same letters used in a different order: for example, MANGO and AMONG. Jesse decided to write a program that finds all anagrams of a given word by generating all possible permutations of its letters and looking up each permutation in a list of words (obtained in a file). If the program can generate and look up 360 permutations per second, how long will it take it to find all anagrams of "BINARY"? "DECIMAL"? What about "CONVERSATION"? ✓

8.4 Using Division

In many combinatorial problems it is easier first to overcount, counting each arrangement several times. This is fine, as long as we count each arrangement the same number of times and know that number. Then we can get the answer by dividing our total count by the number of times we counted each arrangement.

Example 1

n teams are playing in a round-robin tournament; each team plays once with every other team. How many games will be played?

Solution

There are n ways to choose the first team and $(n-1)$ ways to choose the second team for a game. That gives $n(n-1)$. However, this way we have counted each game twice, because it doesn't matter which team is called "first" and which "second." If we swap the two teams we get the same game. Therefore, the answer is $\dfrac{n(n-1)}{2}$.

Example 2

How many words can we make from the letters A L A B A M A (assuming any arrangement of letters is a "word")?

Solution

If all seven letters were different, we would have $7 \cdot 6 \cdot 5 \cdot 4 \cdot 3 \cdot 2 \cdot 1 = 7!$ words. But the four A's are the same, so we get the same word when we permute them. We have counted each arrangement of seven letters the number of times equal to the number of permutations of four A's, that is 4! times. The answer is $\dfrac{7!}{4!} = 5 \cdot 6 \cdot 7 = 210$.

Example 3

There are five identical pairs of gloves in a drawer. If you pull out two gloves at random, what are the odds that they will make a pair?

Solution

We can pull the first glove in 10 ways and the second glove in 9 ways. However, if the order is not important, we have counted each possibility twice. So the total number of ways to choose two gloves is $\dfrac{10 \cdot 9}{2} = 45$. We can pull a left glove in 5 ways and a right glove in 5 ways, so the number of ways to pull out a pair is $5 \cdot 5 = 25$. The number of ways to pull out 2 left gloves is $\dfrac{5 \cdot 4}{2} = 10$. The same for two right gloves. The number of ways to pull out two gloves that don't make a pair is $10 + 10 = 20$. So the numbers match: $25 + 20 = 45$. The odds of getting a pair are $25 : 20 = 5 : 4$ (we say, "5 to 4").

Sometimes, a problem can be solved either by division or by "anchoring" specific properties of an object or an arrangement.

Example 4

How many ways are there to seat a teacher and six students at a round table? Arrangements are considered the same as long as each person has the same left and right neighbors.

Solution

We can say that there are 7! total arrangements and 7 ways to rotate the table, so the answer is equal to $\dfrac{7!}{7} = 6! = 720$.

Another solution may be obtained by sitting down the teacher anywhere at the table; then there are 6! ways to arrange the students.

Exercises

1.   In how many ways can we choose two puppies out of a litter of 12 puppies? ✓

2.   Ice cream comes in two sizes, three flavors, and with any <u>two</u> of five toppings. How many different orders are possible? ✓

3.▪   How many words can we make from the letters T E N N E S S E E (assuming any arrangement of letters is a "word")? ✓

4.▪   How many ways are there to seat a group of six at a rectangular dinner table? The host and the hostess must sit at the short sides and the four guests two at each of the longer sides. Arrangements are considered the same as long as each guest has the same neighbors.

5.▪   In how many ways can we color the six faces of a cube in six different colors? The cube can be rotated any way you want — the colorings are considered the same. ✓

6.♦   An airline is planning three non-stop flights from the East Coast of the United States to the Caribbean. The airline serves six major cities on the East Coast and 12 different Caribbean islands. Two non-stop flights can go to the same island, but they cannot originate at the same East Coast city. How many different configurations of the three flights are possible? ✓

7.♦   How many ways are there to place eight rooks on a chessboard so that none of them threatens any other? A rook moves vertically or horizontally by any number of squares. (The 64 squares on a chessboard are marked "a1" through "h8" and considered different; the eight rooks are considered identical.) ✓

8.5 Combinations

Combinations are selections of k elements from a given set of n elements ($0 \leq k \leq n$), disregarding the order. This number is written $\binom{n}{k}$ and read "*n*-choose-*k*."

$\binom{n}{k}$ are important numbers in mathematics and they have many nice properties. First of all, notice that there is a kind of symmetry: $\binom{n}{k} = \binom{n}{n-k}$. Indeed, to choose k objects is the same as to set aside the remaining $n-k$ objects. Note that $\binom{n}{n} = 1$. Mathematicians have agreed that $\binom{n}{0} = 1$, so the symmetry is complete.

Let's derive a formula (with factorials) for *n*-choose-*k* using the multiplication and division rules. Suppose we choose k objects as follows: we first arrange all n objects in line, then take the first k. The total number of arrangements is $n!$. However, if we rearrange the first k objects and/or the remaining $n-k$ objects, we will end up with the same selection. There are $k!$ ways to rearrange the first k objects and $(n-k)!$ ways to rearrange the remaining $n-k$ objects. So we have counted each selection $k!(n-k)!$ times. Therefore,

$$\binom{n}{k} = \frac{n!}{k!(n-k)!} = \frac{n \cdot (n-1) \cdot \ldots \cdot (n-k+1)}{k \cdot (k-1) \cdot \ldots \cdot 1}$$

It is convenient to define $0!$ as 1, so that the formula works for $k = 0$, too.

It is useful to remember the formulas for $\binom{n}{k}$ for $k = 0$, 1, 2, and 3:

$$\binom{n}{0} = 1$$

$$\binom{n}{1} = n$$

$$\binom{n}{2} = \frac{n(n-1)}{2}$$

$$\binom{n}{3} = \frac{n(n-1)(n-2)}{6}$$

Example 1

How many ways are there to split 4 different pencils between two children, so that each gets two pencils?

Solution

We need to choose two pencils for the first child — the second child gets the other two.

$$\binom{4}{2} = \frac{4 \cdot 3}{2} = 6.$$

Example 2

How many ways are there to choose 5 cards from a deck of 52 cards?

Solution

$$\binom{52}{5} = \frac{52 \cdot 51 \cdot 50 \cdot 49 \cdot 48}{5 \cdot 4 \cdot 3 \cdot 2 \cdot 1} = 2,598,960.$$

Example 3

How many different bit patterns in a byte have exactly three bits set?

Solution

$$\binom{8}{3} = \frac{8 \cdot 7 \cdot 6}{3!} = 56 .$$

❖ ❖ ❖

$\binom{n}{k} = \dfrac{n!}{k!(n-k)!}$ is a neat formula, and it confirms the symmetry $\binom{n}{k} = \binom{n}{n-k}$. It is not practical for some computations, though, because factorials get very large quickly. For computer programs, it is more convenient to rewrite $\binom{n}{k}$ as a product of fractions:

$$\binom{n}{k} = \frac{n}{k} \cdot \frac{n-1}{k-1} \cdot \dots \cdot \frac{n-k+1}{1}$$

Exercises

1.   How many ways are there to order a pizza with three toppings out of five possible toppings? ✓

2.   Write $\binom{4}{k}$ for $k = 0, 1, 2, 3, 4$.

3.   Pat has 40 beads of which 35 are white and 5 are black. The beads are identical, except for the color. How many different bracelets can Pat make using all 40 beads? The ends of a bracelet are asymmetrical: one has a hook and the other an eyelet. ✓

4.■ Write a Python function `nChooseK` that calculates and returns $\binom{n}{k}$ as an int. The function should work for $0 \le k \le n$. ⸮ Hint: use a `float` for the product of fractions, then convert it into an `int`, using the built-in function `round`. Rounding helps avoid tiny inaccuracies in computer arithmetic. ⸮

5.■ How many ways are there to split 9 different stickers among three people, three apiece? ✓

6.■ How many different tic-tac-toe grids have 3 X's and 3 O's? ⸮ Hint: see Question 5. ⸮

7.◆ How many ways are there to make a "full house" Poker hand from a deck of 52 cards? "Full house" is three cards of one rank and a pair of another rank. ✓

8.◆ If you multiply out $\underbrace{(x+1) \cdot ... \cdot (x+1)}_{n \text{ times}}$, what is the coefficient at x^k in the resulting polynomial?

9.◆ Consider the following Boolean expression:

$$((P \land Q) \lor \neg(P \lor Q)) \land ((P \land \neg Q) \lor \neg P)$$

It has three $\land$ and three $\lor$ operators. Suppose we reshuffle these six operators to make new expressions. Show that among all different expressions obtained this way, at least two will have the same truth tables. ⸮ Hint: don't do logic — just count. ⸮

8.6 Using Addition and Subtraction

Addition comes into play when it is easier to split the set of all possible objects or arrangements into two or more disjoint sets, count the arrangements in each of these sets separately, and then add the results.

Example 1

How many ways are there to choose one or two ice cream toppings from five available toppings?

Solution

One topping is not the same as two toppings! There are 5 ways to choose one and $\dfrac{5 \cdot 4}{2} = 10$ ways to choose two. The answer is $5 + 10 = 15$.

Example 2

How many ways are there to schedule two quizzes in a five-day week, if the quizzes cannot be on the same day or on consecutive days?

Solution

If the first quiz is on the first day, the second quiz can be on the third, fourth or fifth day — three possibilities. If the first quiz is on the second day, the second quiz can be on the fourth or fifth day — 2 possibilities. If the first quiz is on the third day, the second quiz must be on the fifth day — 1 possibility. The answer is $3 + 2 + 1 = 6$.

If you have trouble counting objects or arrangements that satisfy a certain condition, you may try to count <u>all</u> possible arrangements, then count the arrangements that <u>do not</u> satisfy the condition and subtract their number from the total.

Example 3

How many ways are there to seat two adults and four kids in a row in a movie theater so that the two adults are not next to each other?

Solution

The total possible number of arrangements is 6! = 720. Let's count the number of arrangements where the adults <u>are</u> sitting together. The number of ways to choose two seats together for the adults is 5; the number of ways to seat the adults in these seats is 2; the number of ways to seat the kids in the remaining four seats is 4!. So the number of arrangements where the adults sit together is 5·2·(4!) = 240. The answer is 720 − 240 = 480.

Exercises

1.   How many triangles are there in the following picture?

        ⸘ Hint: count triangles of different sizes separately. ⸮

2.   How many different ways are there to make 50 cents using quarters, dimes, and nickels? ✓

3.   How many pairs of integers m and n, such that $2 \le m, n \le 12$, have no common factors (except 1)? ✓

4.   Recall that a valid name in Python can consist of upper- and lowercase letters, digits, and underscore characters, but cannot start with a digit. How many valid Python names of length 3 or less are there? ✓

5.▪   The Andover co-ed indoor soccer league tournament requires a 7-member team with at least two women. The Andover Pythons club has 8 men and 5 women. How many ways do the Pythons have to form a tournament team?

6.♦   Given cards 2 through 10 in four suits (36 cards total), how many ways are there to make 21 on three cards? ⸘ Hint: consider separately the cases where all three cards have the same rank, two cards have the same rank, and all three cards have different ranks. ⸮ ✓

7.   How many four-digit numbers have at least one 7 among their digits?
        ⸹ Hint: count the numbers that do not have any 7s. ⸮ ✓

8.   How many positive integers below 1000 are not divisible by 6?

9.✦   In the diagram below, how many different paths lead from *A* to *B*?

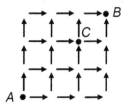

How many of them do not go through point *C*? ✓

10.✦ A password can contain upper- and lowercase letters as well as digits; it must
        include at least one uppercase letter and at least one digit. How many
        different four- or five-character passwords are possible? ✓

8.7 Review

Terms and notation introduced in this chapter:

Combinatorics $1 \cdot 2 \cdot \ldots \cdot n = n!$
Multiplication rule
Permutations $\binom{n}{k} = \dfrac{n!}{k!(n-k)!}$
Factorial
Combinations
n-Choose-k

Some of the Python features introduced in this chapter:

```
round(x)
```

9 Strings, Lists, and Files

9.1 Prologue

You've already seen and worked a little with strings and lists in Python. Now it's time to examine these two types of objects more formally.

In programming languages, a *string* represents a word, a line of text, or any combination of characters. Strings are widely used in processing text documents and text files, as prompts and error messages, and as data elements in objects (for example, a student's name, address, etc.).

A *list* represents... well, a list of items (numbers, objects, etc.). Lists can hold numbers, words, strings, or any other objects (even other lists).

Python treats strings and lists in a unified manner: as "sequences." After all, a string is a sequence of characters and a list is a sequence of items. In Python, a "sequence" is a structure from which we can request items in order. Python has a special statement, called the for loop, that allows us to process all items from a "sequence" in order. For example:

```
>>> s = [7, 3, 5, 8, 0]
>>> for x in s:
        print(x)
7
3
5
8
0
>>> s = 'Python'
>>> for c in s:
        print(c)
P
y
t
h
o
n
```

> **Recall that in is a built-in operator.** c in s **gives** True **if** c **is a character or substring in the string s, or if** c **is an element of the list s.** (in **does not apply to sublists.**)

The characters in a string and the elements of a list are numbered by integers. In Python (as well as in C, C++, Java, and some other languages) the numbering starts from 0. A character's or element's number is called its *index*. If s is a "sequence," s[i] refers to the element with the index *i*. s[0] refers to the first element of the sequence.

In Python you can also use negative indices — then you start counting at the end: s[-1] is the last element, s[-2] is the next to last, and so on.

s[m:n] creates a "slice" of s: a substring or sublist of s. A slice is a new sequence made up of the items s[m], s[m+1], ..., s[n-1]. Note that s[n] is not included. For example:

```
>>> s = [7,3,5,8,0]
>>> s[1:4]
[3, 5, 8]
>>> s = 'Python'
>>> s[2:5]
'tho'
```

> **The slice** s[m:n] **has** n-m **elements.**

> **The built-in function** len(s) **returns the length of s; that is, the number of characters in the string or the number of elements in the list.**

s[-1] is the same as s[len(s)-1].

9.2 Strings

Python uses Unicode to represent strings. A Unicode string represents each character in two bytes. It can encode up to 65,000 characters, enough to encode the alphabets of most world languages and many special characters. For example, hex 20ac represents the euro currency symbol '€'. You can enter this symbol in a string as '\u20ac'. Try:

```
>>> print('Pecorino di Pienza \u20ac' + str(3.95) + " l'etto")
Pecorino di Pienza €3.95 l'etto
```

Unicode has a provision to extend the character set even further, into millions of different codes.

> **In Python a character is treated as a string that consists of one character. So, technically speaking, s[i] is a substring of s.**

Python has many functions that help you work with strings. These functions are implemented in the object-oriented programming (OOP) manner. In OOP, functions are called *methods*, and they are viewed as attached to individual objects.

> **The syntax for calling methods is different: instead of writing someFun(s) we write s.someFun(). someFun(s,x) becomes s.someFun(x). This emphasizes the fact that the first argument is special: it is the object whose method is called.**

For example, s.find(sub) returns the index of the first occurrence of the substring sub in s. s.find(sub, start) returns the first occurrence after the index start.

> **One exception is len, which is a built-in function in Python. We have to write len(s), because len is not a method of s.**

> **Strings are immutable objects. This means none of a string's methods can change its contents.**

Consider, for example the method upper, which converts all letters in the string into the upper case. At the first glance, it may seem that s.upper() changes s. But it does not:

```
>>> s = 'amy'
>>> s.upper()
'AMY'
>>> s
'amy'
```

What's going on? s.upper() creates a new string 'AMY' and returns a reference to it, but s remains unchanged. Now try this:

```
>>> s = 'amy'
>>> s2 = s.upper()
>>> s
'amy'
>>> s2
'AMY'
```

To change s to upper case, you need:

```
>>> s = s.upper()
```

Now s refers to the new string. The old string is recycled by the Python's *garbage collector*.

Appendix C summarizes the more commonly used string methods. There are methods that verify whether the string consists of characters from a given category (all letters, all digits, all alphanumeric characters, all white space, etc.), methods that convert the string to upper and lower case, methods that justify the string on the left, right, or in the center of a wider string, methods that find a given substring (or character) in the string, and so on.

Example 1

Write a function that takes a string in the form `'x + y'` and converts it into *postfix notation* `'x y +'`, where x and y are any names, possibly surrounded by spaces or tabs. For example, `toPostfix('   num +   incr\n')` should return `'num incr +'`.

Solution

```
def toPostfix(s):
    k = s.find('+')
    return s[0:k].strip() + ' ' + s[k+1:].strip() + ' +'
```

`k = s.find('+')` sets k to the index of the first occurrence of `'+'` in s. `s2.strip()` removes the white space at the beginning and the end of s2. Here strip is called for substrings of s: `s[0:k]` and `s[k+1:]`. `s[k+1:]` returns the tail of the string starting at `s[k+1]` — the same as `s[k+1:len(s)]`.

Example 2

Write a function that takes a date in the format m/d/yyyy and returns it in the format dd-mm-yyyy. (In the input string, *m* and *d* represent one- or two-digit numbers for month and day, respectively; in the output string, *mm* and *dd* are two digit numbers.) For example, `convertDate('7/17/2009')` should return `'17-07-2009'`.

Solution

```
def convertDate(date):
    k1 = date.find('/')
    k2 = date.rfind('/')
    return date[k1+1:k2].zfill(2) + '-' + date[0:k1].zfill(2) + \
                 '-' + date[k2+1:]
```

`s.rfind(sub)` finds the position of the <u>last</u> occurrence of `sub` in `s`. `s.zfill(n)` pads `s` with zeros on the left to make a string of length n.

Example 3

Write a function that replaces every occurrence of `'<b>'` with `'<i>'` and every occurrence of `'</b>'` with `'</i>'` in a given string and returns a new string. For example, `boldToItalic('Strings are <b>immutable</b> objects')` should return `'Strings are <i>immutable</i> objects')`.

Solution

```
def boldToItalic(text):
    return text.replace('<b>', '<i>').replace('</b>', '</i>')
```

`s.replace(old, new)` replaces every occurrence of `old` in `s` with `new`. Don't be surprised by the two dot operators chained in one statement: since `text.replace(...)` returns a string, we can call that string's methods.

Exercises

1.   Python strings have methods `s.startswith(sub)` and
        `s.endswith(sub)`, which return `True` if s starts with `sub` or ends with
        `sub`, respectively. Pretend that these methods do not exist and write your
        own functions `startswith(s,sub)` and `endswith(s,sub)`. Do not use
        loops in your functions: use only string methods. Test your functions and
        make sure they work the same way as the `startswith` and `endswith`
        methods, including the cases when `sub` is an empty string and when `sub` is
        the same as `s`. ✓

2.   Write and test a function that corrects the "two caps" typo: if a string starts
        with two capital letters followed by a lowercase letter, the function should
        change the second letter to lower case and return the new string; otherwise it
        should return the original string unchanged.

3.   Write and test a function `getDigits(s)` that returns a string of all digits
        found in s (in the same order). For example, `getDigits('**1.23a-42')`
        should return `'12342'`. ✓

4.   Write and test a function that takes a string of digits and returns a new string
        with the leading zeros removed.

5.■   Recall that a valid name in Python can have letters, digits, and underscore
        characters and cannot start with a digit. Write a function `isValidName(s)`
        that returns `True` if s represents a valid name in Python; otherwise your
        function should return `False`. Test your function on the following strings:

Valid:	Invalid:
`'bDay'`	`'1a'`
`'A0'`	`'#A'`
`'_a_1'`	`'1_a'`
`'_1amt'`	`'[a]'`
`'__'`	`' ABC'`
`'_'`	`' '`
	`'A#'`
	`'A-2'`
	`'a_5+'`

6.■ Write a function `isValidAmt(s)` that returns `True` if the string `s` represents a valid dollar amount. Otherwise the function should return `False`. A valid amount string is allowed to have white space at the beginning and at the end; the remaining characters must be digits, with the possible exception of one decimal point. If a decimal point is present, it must have at least one digit before it and it must be followed by exactly two digits. For example:

Valid:	Invalid:
`'123.45'`	`'$123.45'`
`'   123.45   '`	`'123.'`
`'   123'`	`'1.23.'`
`'123'`	`'   123.0'`
`'      0.45'`	`'.5'`
`'0'`	`'+0.45'`

Be sure to test your function with all of the above.

7.■ Write and test a function `removeTag(s)` that tries to find within `s` the first substring enclosed within angle brackets, removes it (including the angle brackets) if found, and returns a new string. For example, `removeTag('Do <u>not</u> disturb')` should return `'Do not</u> disturb'`. If no angle brackets are found, the function should return the original string unchanged. ✓

8.■ Write and test a function `removeAllTags(s)` that finds and removes from `s` all substrings enclosed within angle brackets. ⸮ Hint: you can call `removeTag` from Question 7. ⸮

9.■ A postal code in Canada has the format "ADA DAD" where A is any letter and D is any digit. For example: L3P 7P5. It may have zero, one, or two spaces between the first and the second triplet. Write a function that verifies whether a given string has the right format for a valid Canadian postal code, and if so, returns it with all spaces removed and all the letters converted to upper case. If the format is not valid, the function should return an empty string. Create a comprehensive set of test strings and test your function on that set.

9.3   Lists and Tuples

In Python a list is written within square brackets, with elements separated by commas. A list can have elements of different types mixed together. For example:

```
[3, 'Large fries', 2.29]
```

The indices, slices, `in` operator, and `len` work for lists in the same manner as for strings.

> **lst[:] returns a copy of lst. It is the same as lst[0:len(lst)] or lst[0:] or lst[:len(lst)].**

The built-in functions `min(lst)` and `max(lst)` return the smallest and the largest element in the list `lst`, respectively. All the elements of `lst` must be comparable to each other. What is smaller and what is larger depends on the type of objects. Strings, for example, are ordered alphabetically, but all upper case letters are "smaller" than all lower case letters.

The + operator applied to two lists concatenates them. For example:

```
>>> [1,2,3] + [4,5]
[1, 2, 3, 4, 5]
```

Python also has a built-in function `list(s)` that converts a "sequence" (for example, a string) s into a list and returns that list. Do not use the name `list` for your variables.

> **Lists are <u>not</u> immutable: a list has methods that can change it.**

A list has methods that insert and remove elements from it, find a given value, reverse the list, and sort the list (arrange its elements in order). For example:

```
>>> lst=[1, 3, 2]
>>> lst.sort()
>>> lst
[1, 2, 3]
>>> lst.reverse()
>>> lst
[3, 2, 1]
```

Appendix D summarizes some commonly used list methods.

The `lst.index(x)` method returns the index of the first element in `lst` that is equal to `x`. When `x` is not in `lst`, this method raises an exception. So it may be necessary to check first whether `x` is in `lst`:

```
if x in lst:
    i = lst.index(x)
else:
    ...
```

(A string also has a method called `index`. Like `lst.index(x)`, `s.index(x)` raises an exception when the target is not found. So it is usually better to use `s.find`, which returns -1 when the target is not found. Lists do not have a method `find`.)

> **The statement `del lst[i]` removes `lst[i]` from the list `lst`. You can also remove a slice: `del lst[i:j]`.**

For example:

```
>>> lst = ['A', 'B', 'C', 'D', 'E']
>>> del lst[1:3]
>>> lst
['A', 'D', 'E']
```

Example 1

Write a function that swaps the first and last elements of a given list.

Solution

```
def swapFirstLast(lst):
    n = len(lst) - 1
    temp = lst[0]
    lst[0] = lst[n]
    lst[n] = temp
```

Example 2

Write a function that rotates a list, moving its first element to the end.

Solution

```
def rotateLeft(lst):              Or        def rotateLeft(lst):
    n = len(lst) - 1                             n = len(lst)-1
    temp = lst[0]                                temp = lst[0]
    i = 1                                        lst[0:n] = lst[1:n+1]
    while  i <= n:                               lst[n] = temp
        lst[i-1] = lst[i]
        i += 1
    lst[n] = temp
```

❖   ❖   ❖

We often need to apply the same formula or function to each element of a list and create a new list that contains these modified elements. Python has a feature known as *list comprehensions*, which automates such procedures. A "list comprehension" is a statement that constructs a new list from a given list by applying a formula or a function (or some expression) to each element. For example:

```
resultLst = [2*x for x in lst]
```

This is the same as:

```
resultLst = []
for x in lst:
    resultLst.append(2*x)
```

Another example:

```
lengths = [len(w) for w in words]
```

If `words = ['All', 'is', 'well']`, then `lengths` becomes `[3, 2, 4]`.

This is the same as:

```
lengths = []
for w in words:
    lengths.append(len(w))
```

You can also apply a condition to the elements and include in the resulting list only the elements for which the condition is true. For example:

```
>>> nums = [-1, -4, 2, 5, -3, 11]
>>> positives = [x for x in nums if x > 0]
>>> positives
[2, 5, 11]
```

Example 3

Write a function that takes a list of words and creates a new list of words choosing only those words whose length is not less then 3 and not greater than 5.

Solution

```
def chooseLength3_5(words):
    return [w for w in words if 3 <= len(w) <= 5]
```

(In Python you can combine two relational operators in one expression, as in a < x <= b. We have not done this before, because this feature is not common in other programming languages, and we didn't want you to acquire a "bad habit." But here it fits too well to resist.)

As we said earlier, lists are not immutable: a list has methods that add and remove elements, etc. A *tuple* is a Python object that represents an immutable list. A tuple is written by placing its elements in parentheses, separating them by commas. For example: (3, 4, 5). The [], +, and in operators work for tuples the same way as for lists, but tuples have no methods except count and index. Tuples are convenient when you need to return several values from a function — you can combine them into one tuple.

Example 4

Write a function that takes a list of words and returns a tuple containing the shortest and the longest word.

Solution

```
def shortestAndLongest(words):
    iShort, iLong = 0, 0
    i = 1
    while i < len(words):
        if len(words[i]) < len(words[iShort]):
            iShort = i
        if len(words[i]) > len(words[iLong]):
            iLong = i
        i += 1
    return (words[iShort], words[iLong])
```

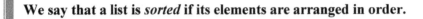

We say that a list is *sorted* if its elements are arranged in order.

Sorting is a very common operation. For example, if you have two mailing lists and you want to merge them into one and eliminate duplicate records, it is better to sort each list first. There are several sorting algorithms, ranging from very straightforward (see Question 6) to more advanced.

Exercises

1.   Pretend that list's `reverse` method does not exist and write your own function `reverseList(lst)` that reverses the list in place and returns None. ⸱ Hints: proceed from both ends, but not too far... No need for a `return` statement. ⸱ ✓

2.   Write and test a function that returns the index of the largest element in the list (or, if several elements have the largest value, the index of the first one of them). Do not use the built-in function `max`. ⸱ Hint: see Example 4. ⸱

3.■   Write and test a function that takes a list with three or more elements and returns the index of the element that makes the greatest sum with its left and right neighbors.

4.   Replace the following code with a list comprehension:

```
nums1 = []
for x in nums:
    nums1.append(x + 1)
```

✓

5.   Write and test a function `allPairs(n)` that returns the list of all $\dfrac{n(n-1)}{2}$ tuples `(i, j)`, where $1 \le i < j \le n$. For example, `allPairs(3)` should return `[(1,2), (1,3), (2,3)]`.

6.■   Pretend that list's `sort` method does not exist and write your own function `sort(a)` that sorts the list `a` in ascending order (and returns `None`). Use the following algorithm (called *Selection Sort*):

> Set *n* equal to `len(a)`
> Repeat the following steps while *n* > 1:
>   Find the largest among the first *n* elements (see Example 4)
>   Swap it with the *n*-th element
>   Decrement *n* by 1

7.◆   The function below takes sorted lists `a` and `b` and merges all the elements from `b` into `a`, so that the resulting list is sorted:

```
def merge(a, b):
    for x in b:
        i = 0
        while i < len(a) and x > a[i]:
            i += 1
        a.insert(i, x)
```

If `a = [1, 3, 5, ..., 199]` and `b = [2, 4, 6, ..., 200]`, how many times will the comparison `x > a[i]` be executed in `merge(a, b)`? Make a couple of minor changes to the above code to improve its efficiency: `x > a[i]` should be executed no more than 200 times for these lists. ⸂ Hint: move one line and add one line of code. ⸃ ✓

8.◆   Research the Mastermind game on the Internet and write a program that models the Mastermind board and acts as the game leader, so that you can play Mastermind with the computer. Use the letters A, B, C, D, E, F for colors, and the letters X and O for black and white pegs, respectively. The computer should choose a configuration of 4 letters randomly. ⸂ Hint: recall that `choice(lst)` returns a randomly chosen element of `lst`. `choice` is in the `random` module, so you need `from random import choice`. ⸃

9.4   Files

A *file* is a collection of related data stored on a computer's hard disk or another digital device or computer-readable media. A file can store a text document, a tune, an image, a video clip, the source code for a program, and so on. Computer programs can read files and create new files.

A file is identified by its name and extension. The extension often identifies the format and/or purpose of the file. For example in `Birthdays.py`, the extension `py` tells us that this file holds the source code for a Python program, and in `graduation.jpg`, the extension `.jpg` tells us that this file holds an image in the JPEG format. In general, when a program creates a file, it is up to that program to decide how the data will be organized in the file. But there are some standard file formats that many different programs understand. You have probably encountered `.mp3` files for music, `.jpg` files for images, `.doc` files for *Word* documents, `.htm` or `.html` files for web pages, and so on.

All files fall into two broad categories: *text files* and *binary files*. A text file holds lines of text, separated by end-of-line markers. The characters in a text file are encoded in one of the standard encodings, such as ASCII (read 'as-kee') or one of the Unicode encodings. An end-of-line marker is usually a newline character `'\n'`, a carriage return character `'\r'`, or their combination, `'\r\n'`. Files with the extensions `.txt`, `.html`, and `.py` are examples of text files.

A binary file holds any kind of data, basically a sequence of bytes — there is no assumption that the file holds lines of text (although you can treat a text file as a binary file, if you wish). `.mp3`, `.jpg`, and `.doc` files are examples of binary files.

An operating system organizes files into a system of nested folders (also called *directories*) and allows users to move, copy, rename, and delete files. Each operating system also provides services to programs for reading and writing files. Programming languages usually include libraries of functions for dealing with files. Here we will use only Python's built-in functions for reading and writing text files.

To open a text file in a Python program, use the built-in function `open`. For example:

```
f = open('GreenEggs.txt')
```

> **The file must be in the folder that the Python interpreter uses as its current directory. See Appendix A at www.skylit.com/python for instructions on how to choose that folder.**

Alternatively you can specify the *absolute pathname* of the file. For example:

```
f = open('C:/mywork/GreenEggs.txt')
```

This is not recommended, however, because your program will stop working if the file is moved to a different folder or the folder is renamed.

> **When you have finished working with the file, you have to close it:**
>
> `f.close()`

When a text file is open for reading, Python treats it as a sequence of lines. To read the next line, use file's `readline` method. Try, for example:

```
>>> f = open('greeneggs.txt')
>>> line = f.readline()
>>> line
'I am Sam\n'
```

> **Note that Python leaves the newline character '\n' in the string read from a file. If there are no more lines left in the file, `readline` returns an empty string.**

The easiest way to read and process all the lines from a text file is with a `for` loop:

```
for line in f:
    ...  # process line
```

Example 1

```
for line in f:
    print(line, end='')
```

The `end=''` parameter tells `print` not to add a newline character to the output. We want it here because every line read from a file already has a newline character at the end. Without `end=''` the file will be printed out double-spaced.

A file object also has the method `readlines`, which reads all the lines from the file and returns a list of all the lines read.

Example 2

```
>>> f = open('greeneggs.txt')
>>> lines = f.readlines()
>>> f.close()
>>> len(lines)
19
>>> lines[0]
'I am Sam\n'
>>> lines[1]
'Sam I am\n'
>>> lines[-1]
'I do not like them, Sam-I-am.\n'
```

If possible, read a file line by line. Avoid reading the whole file into a list because a file may be quite large.

None of the "read" methods skip empty lines; an empty line is returned as `'\n'`.

To create a file for writing, add a second argument, `'w'`, to the call to `open`. Use file's `write` method to write a string to a file.

Example 3:

```
f = open('story.txt', 'w')
f.write('I do not like\n')
f.write('green eggs and ham.\n')
f.close()
```

The result is a file called `story.txt` that contains

```
I do not like
green eggs and ham.
```

Be careful: if you open for writing a file that already exists, it will be reduced to zero size and the old information in the file will be lost!

Don't forget to close the file when you have finished writing into it. If you forget to close the file, some of the information may not be written into it.

Instead of `f.write(s)`, you can use `print(s, file=f)`. As you know, `print` adds one newline character at the end of each line (unless a trailing comma is supplied in the `print` statement), so you don't have to supply `'\n'` in the lines you print.

Example 4

```
f = open('story.txt', 'w')
print('I do not like', file=f)
print('green eggs and ham.', file=f)
f.close()
```

Example 5

```
f = open('transactions.txt', 'w')
qty = 3
price = 2.95
amt = qty * price
print(' {0:4d}  {1:5.2f} {2:7.2f}'.format(qty, price, amt), file=f)
qty = 4
price = 1.85
amt = qty * price
print(' {0:4d}  {1:5.2f} {2:7.2f}'.format(qty, price, amt), file=f)
f.close()
```

This creates a file `transactions.txt` that contains

```
   3   2.95    8.85
   4   1.85    7.40
```

Exercises

1.   Write a program that reads a text file and displays it with a line number at the beginning of each line. ✓

2.   Write a program that creates a copy of a text file. Your program should prompt the user to enter the names of the input and output files.

3.   Write a program that reads a given file and displays all the lines that contain a given string.

4.■   You have two input files, each sorted in the order established by the `<=` operator: if `line1` is earlier in the file than `line2`, then `line1 <= line2` is true. (This ordering is basically alphabetical, except any uppercase letter is "smaller" then any lowercase letter.) Write and test a program that merges these files into one sorted file. Do not load the files into memory — read them line by line.

5.■ Write a program that counts the occurrences of the 26 English letters, case-blind, in a text file and displays their relative frequencies. The program should prompt the user for a file name, count the number of occurrences of each letter, and display each letter, along with its frequency expressed as percentage of the total number of letters. The letters should be displayed in order of frequency. For example, if the file contains two 'A's and three 'B's, and no other letters, then the output should be:

```
Text file name: madlibs.txt
B: 60.0
A: 40.0
C:  0.0
...
Z:  0.0
```

& Hints:

1. Allocate a list of 26 counts, initially set to 0: `counts = 26*[0]`

2. Read the file one line at a time. For each line read, increment the appropriate count for each letter in the line. The index of the count to be incremented is the index of the letter (converted to the upper case) in `abc = 'ABCDEFGHIJKLMNOPQRSTUVWXYZ'`.

3. The built-in `sum` function returns the sum of all the elements of a list.

4. Use a list comprehension to create a list of frequencies, expressed as percentages of the total number of letters.

5. Create a list of (percent, letter) pairs. The built-in function `zip(s1, s2)` combines the respective elements from the sequences `s1` and `s2` into pairs (tuples) and generates a sequence of such tuples. For example, `list(zip([60.0, 40.0], ['B', 'A']))` returns `[(60.0, 'B'), (40.0, 'A')]`.

6. Sort the list of pairs — it will be sorted by the first element in each pair.

7. Print out both elements of each pair in the desired format. (Reverse the list to obtain the descending order or print the list in reverse order.)

6.♦   Write a function `anagrams(w, words)` that finds all anagrams for a given word `w` in the list `words`. The function should return a list of pairs (`w`, `w2`), where `w2` is an anagram of `w`. Write a program that prompts the user to enter a word and displays all anagrams for that word found in a file of words. If no anagrams are found, the program should display an empty list `[]`. The file of words, `words.txt`, is provided in `Py\Ch09`. Example:

```
Enter a word: later
[('LATER', 'ALERT'), ('LATER', 'ALTER')]
```

or

```
Enter a word: charisma
[('CHARISMA', 'ARCHAISM')]
```

⸙ Hints:

1. `words.txt` has one word per line. Use `f.readlines()` to read all the words into a list.

2. Use a list comprehension to strip white space from each word and convert it to upper case.

3. Use `list(w)` to convert `w` into a list of letters, then sort that list.

4. Use the `==` operator to compare two sorted lists of letters.

5. Avoid counting the word itself as its own anagram.

⸜

7.♦   Using the code from Question 6, write a program that finds all pairs of words in `words.txt` that are anagrams of each other. Be very patient: it may take several minutes to get the result. Can you think of some ways to speed up your program?

8.♦   In the Mad Libs™ party game, the leader has the text of a short story with a few missing words in it. The missing words are tagged by their part of speech or function: <noun>, <verb>, <place>, etc. For example:

```
It was a <adjective> summer day.
Jack was sitting in a <place>.
...
```

The leader examines the text and prompts the players for the missing words:

```
Please give me an/a:
adjective
place
...
```

She then reads the text with the supplied words inserted into their respective places.

Write a program that acts as a Mad Libs leader. It should prompt the user for a file name, read the text from the file, find the tags for the missing words (anything within <...>), prompt the user for these words, and save them in a list. It should then reopen the file and display the completed text, inserting the saved words in place of the corresponding tags. A sample file, madlibs.txt, is provided in Py\Ch09. ⸮ Hint: you can read the text line by line, as long as tags are not split between lines. Save the entered substitutions in a list. ⸮

9.5   Review

Terms introduced in this chapter:

String	*File*
List	*Text file*
Tuple	*Binary file*
Index	
Method	

Some of the Python features introduced in this chapter:

```
s[i],s[i:j],s[i:]
s.isalpha(),s.isdigit(),s.isalnum(),...
s.upper(),s.lower(),...
s.replace(old, new),s.strip()
s.find(sub),s.rfind(sub),s.count(sub)

lst=[]
lstCopy = lst[:]
lst.append(x),lst.insert(i, x),lst.pop(),lst.pop(i)
lst.remove(x)
lst.reverse(),lst.sort()
[g(x) for x in lst]
[g(x) for x in lst if ...]

(a, b, c)

f = open('MyInputFile')
f.readline(),f.readlines()
for line in f:
    ... # process line

f = open('MyOutputFile', 'w')
f.write(s)
print(line, file=f)

f.close()
```

10 Parity, Invariants, and Finite Strategy Games

10.1 Prologue

Suppose you are buying a box of cereal in a grocery store. The cashier runs the box through the scanner, which reads the UPC (Universal Product Code) barcode from it. Sometimes an error occurs, and the cashier has to scan the same item again. But how does the system know that an error has occurred? If it read the UPC incorrectly, it could potentially charge you for a can of tuna instead of the box of cereal. Well, it turns out that not all 12-digit numbers are valid UPCs. In fact, if you change any one digit in a UPC, you will get an invalid code that does not match any product. This is because not all digits in a UPC carry information: the last digit is the *check digit*, which depends on the previous digits. If you change one digit in a UPC, the check digit no longer matches the code. We can say that a UPC has built-in *redundancy*: the information is not represented with optimal efficiency. The check digit is redundant because it can be computed from the other digits. Redundancy allows us to detect and sometimes even correct errors.

When we store or transmit binary data, we can stipulate that the number of 1's in each byte be even (or odd). Only seven bits in each byte would then carry information; the eighth bit would be used as a kind of check digit. It is called the *parity bit*. We will discuss parity and check digits in Section 10.2.

Suppose the data is encoded in bytes with *even parity*. This means the total number of bits set to '1' in each byte is even. If a quantity or property remains constant throughout a process, such a quantity or property is called an *invariant*. The sum of the angles in any triangle is 180 degrees. This is an invariant. If within a `while` loop you add 1 to `m` and subtract 1 from `k`, after each iteration the sum `m + k` remains unchanged. This is an invariant. We will talk about invariants and their role in mathematics and computer science in Section 10.3.

A *finite strategy game* for two players is a game with a finite number of possible positions. Two players take turns advancing from one position to the next, according to the rules of the game. Positions never repeat; that is, it is not possible to return to a position visited earlier. Some of the positions are designated as winning positions: the player who reaches a winning position first wins. If neither of the players can make a valid move and neither has reached a winning position, then it is a tie. Tic-tac-toe is an example of a finite strategy game.

In strategy games of this kind, either the first or the second player always has a winning strategy, or both have a strategy that leads to a tie. In games where a tie is not possible, it is often desirable to describe the winning strategy using some invariant — a property shared by all the winning positions, and by all *safe* positions where the winning player can land. The losing player is always forced to abandon a safe position and move into an *unsafe* one. Nim is an example of such a game. We will discuss the details and see some examples of finite games and their strategies, including Nim, in Section 10.4.

10.2 Parity and Checksums

If you store binary data or send information over a communication line, some errors might occur. A simple method for detecting errors is based on *parity*. Usually the data is divided into relatively short sequences of bits, called *codewords* or *packets*.

> The term *parity* refers to the evenness or oddness of the number of bits set to '1' in a packet. If this number is even, we say that the packet has *even parity*; otherwise we say it has *odd parity*.

When a chunk of data is transmitted, the transmitter computes the parity of data and adds one bit (called *parity bit*), so that the total parity of the packet including the parity bit is even. Then, if the receiver gets a packet with odd parity, it reports an error. (The transmitter and receiver may "agree" to use odd parity instead of even parity.) When parity is used, all data packets usually have the same length. For example, seven data bits plus one parity bit or 31 data bits plus one parity bit.

Example 1

The following sequence of seven-bit codes encodes the word "parity" in ASCII:

```
1110000 1100001 1110010 1101001 1110100 1111001
```

We want to add a parity bit to each code so that it gets even parity. What are the resulting eight-bit packets?

Solution

```
11100001 11000011 11100100 11010010 11101000 11110011
```

It can happen, of course, that two errors occur in the same packet — two bits are flipped from 0 to 1 or from 1 to 0. Then the parity of the packet remains unchanged, and the error goes undetected. The parity method relies on the assumption that the likelihood of two errors in the same packet is really low. If errors are frequent, then a small number of bits require a parity bit for error checking. The more reliable a communication channel or a storage system is, the longer the data packets that can be used.

If we swap two consecutive bits in a data packet, its parity does not change. Luckily such *transposition errors* are very rare when the packet is generated by a computer or another device. Not so with us humans. When we type words or numbers, transposition errors are common. So parity-type error detection does not work well when humans are involved. For example, when a cashier gives up on the scanner that cannot read the UPC from a crumpled bag of chips, he enters it manually. The cashier may mistype a digit or transpose two digits. There must be a mechanism that detects such errors. Such a mechanism uses *checksums* and *check digits*.

Example 2

Driver's licenses on the island of Azkaban have six digits. The sixth digit is the check digit: it is calculated as follows: we add up the first five digits, take the resulting sum modulo 10 (the remainder when the sum is divided by 10), and subtract that number from 10. For example, if the first five digits of a driver's license are 95873, the check digit is $10 - ((9 + 5 + 8 + 7 + 3) \bmod 10) = 10 - (32 \bmod 10) = 10 - 2 = 8$. So 958738 is a valid driver's license number on Azkaban. Note that if we add all six digits and take the result modulo 10, we get 0. Does this system detect all single-digit substitution errors? All transposition errors?

Solution

This system detects all single-digit substitution errors, because if you change one digit, the sum of the digits modulo 10 is no longer 0. However, the sum does not depend on the order of digits, so transposition errors are not detected.

To detect both substitution and transposition errors we need a slightly more elaborate algorithm for calculating the check digit. We can multiply some of the digits by certain coefficients before adding them to the sum. Several real-world checksum algorithms are described in the exercises.

Exercises

1. Which of the following bit packets have even parity? Odd parity?
    (a) 01100010 (b) 11010111 (c) 10110001. ✓

2. How many bytes (all possible eight-bit combinations of 0s and 1s) have even parity? Odd parity? ✓

3. Section 8.5 describes the n-choose-k numbers $\binom{n}{k}$. For any given $n \geq 1$, the sum of $\binom{n}{k}$ for all even k is the same as the sum of $\binom{n}{k}$ for all odd k. For example, for $n = 4$, $\binom{4}{0} + \binom{4}{2} + \binom{4}{4} = \binom{4}{1} + \binom{4}{3}$. Indeed, $1 + 6 + 1 = 4 + 4$.
    Why is this true for any $n \geq 1$? ⸮ Hint: see Question 2. ⸮ ✓

4. Write and test a Python function that takes a string of binary digits and returns its parity (as an integer, 0 for even, 1 for odd).

5. Consider the following table of binary digits:

    ```
    0 1 1 0 1 1
    1 0 0 0 1 0
    1 0 1 0 0 1
    0 1 0 1 0 0
    ```

    It was supposed to have even parity in all rows and all columns, but an error occurred and one bit got flipped. Which one? ✓

6.■   Write and test a Python function `correctError(t)`, which takes a table, such as described in Question 5 (but not necessarily 4 by 6), with a possible single-bit error, checks whether it has an error, and, if so, corrects it. The table `t` is represented as a list of its rows; each row is represented as a string of 0s and 1s (all the strings have the same length). For example, the table from Question 5 would be represented as

```
['011011', '100010', '101001', '010100']
```

7.■   How many 4 by 6 tables of binary digits have even parity in all rows and all columns? Odd parity? ✓

8.■   The UPC has 12 decimal digits. The checksum is calculated as follows: we take the sum of all the digits in odd positions, starting from the left (first, third, fifth, etc.), multiply it by 3, then add the sum of all the digits in even positions (second, fourth, etc.). In a valid UPC, the checksum must be evenly divisible by 10. For example, `072043000187` is a valid UPC, because $0 \cdot 3 + 7 + 2 \cdot 3 + 0 + 4 \cdot 3 + 3 + 0 \cdot 3 + 0 + 0 \cdot 3 + 1 + 8 \cdot 3 + 7 = 60$, which is evenly divisible by 10. Write and test a Python function `isValidUPC(s)` that takes a string of 12 digits and returns `True` if it represents a valid UPC; otherwise it returns `False`.

9.   Does the checksum method for UPCs, described in Question 8, detect all single-digit substitution errors?

10.■   In the UPC checksum algorithm, described in Question 8, the odd-placed digits are multiplied by 3. Why 3 and not 2? ✓

11.◆   Does the checksum method for UPCs, described in Question 8, detect all transposition errors?

12.■   Credit card numbers have 16 digits. The checksum is calculated as follows. Each digit in an odd position (first, third, etc.) is multiplied by 2. If the result is a two-digit number, its two digits are added together; otherwise it is left alone. The result is added to the sum. Each digit in an even position (second, fourth, etc.) is added to the sum as is. The resulting sum must be 0 modulo 10. For example, `4111111111111111` is a valid credit card number: its checksum is 30. `4111111111111178` is another valid number: its checksum is 40. Write and test a Python function that checks whether a given string of 16 digits represents a valid credit card number. Come up with a few other valid numbers and use a few invalid numbers for testing.

13. ■ The book industry uses ISBNs (International Standard Book Numbers) to identify books. In 2007 the industry switched from 10-digit ISBNs to 13-digit ISBNs. The last digit in ISBN-10 and in ISBN-13 is the check digit. But the algorithms for calculating the check digit are different for ISBN-10 and ISBN-13.

In ISBN-13, the check digit is calculated the same way as in UPC, only the positions of the digits are counted starting from 0. The first digit is added to the sum as is, the second digit is multiplied by 3, the third digit is added as is, the fourth is multiplied by 3, and so on.

ISBN-13 is obtained from ISBN-10 by appending '978' at the beginning and recalculating the check digit.

Write a Python function `isbn13CheckDigit` that calculates and returns the ISBN-13 check digit (a single character) for a given string of 12 digits, and another function, `isbn10to13`, that converts ISBN-10 (a string of 10 digits) to ISBN-13 and returns a string of 13 digits. Test your functions thoroughly. Use these test data, for example:

ISBN-10	ISBN-13
0982477503	9780982477502
0982477511	9780982477519
098247752X	9780982477526
0982477538	9780982477533
0982477546	9780982477540
0982477554	9780982477557
0982477562	9780982477564
0982477570	9780982477571
0982477589	9780982477588
0982477597	9780982477595

14. ■ Question 13 asks you to write two functions that help convert ISBN-10 to ISBN-13. Now write two similar functions to convert ISBN-13 to ISBN-10. In ISBN-10, the check digit is calculated as follows. The first digit is multiplied by 1, the second by 2, the third by 3, and so on; the ninth digit is multiplied by 9. The products are added together and the result is divided by 11 with the remainder. The remainder is used as the check digit. If the remainder is 10, the letter 'X' is used as the check "digit."

10.3 Invariants

If I have several lollipops and give you some, and you give some to Candy, and she gives some back to me and you, the total number of lollipops among the three of us remains the same (as long as we don't eat any) — it is an *invariant*. If a particle moves along a circle, its distance from the center of the circle remains constant — it is an invariant. If a bishop moves on the chessboard along a north-east to south-west diagonal, the sum of the bishop's row and column positions, counting from the upper-left corner, remains the same — it is an invariant. The concept of invariant is useful in physics, in mathematics, and in computer science.

Example 1

If you toss a small rock in the air, its energy consists of the kinetic energy $\dfrac{mv^2}{2}$ and the potential energy mgh, where m is the mass of the rock, v is its speed, h is the height above ground, and $g = 9.8$ m/sec^2 is the acceleration due to gravity. How far up above the ground will the rock fly if it was tossed straight up from ground level with an initial velocity of 20 m/sec?

Solution

$\dfrac{mv^2}{2} + mgh$ is an invariant, it remains constant. So $\dfrac{mv_0^2}{2} + mgh_0 = \dfrac{mv_1^2}{2} + mgh_1$

At the beginning, $h_0 = 0$, $v_0 = 20$ m/sec. At the top, $v_1 = 0$. Comparing the total energy at the ground and at the top, we get $\dfrac{mv_0^2}{2} = mgh_1 \;\Rightarrow\; h_1 = \dfrac{v_0^2}{2g} \approx 20.4$ meters.

In mathematics, invariants are ubiquitous. One of the applications is in strategy games.

Example 2

There is a round table in a room and three bags of coins: one with quarters, one with dimes, and one with nickels. Two players take turns, picking one coin from any bag and placing it anywhere on the table, without overlapping any other coins. There are enough coins in each bag to cover the entire table. The player who places the last coin, leaving no space for more coins, wins. Does the first or a second player have a winning strategy?

Solution

In this game, there is an infinite number of possible configurations of coins on the table. But the game always ends after several moves, because only a finite number of coins fit on the table. There are no ties.

One approach to finding a strategy in games of this type is to come up with a clever invariant condition, a kind of "balance," which the winner can maintain, always moving into a safe position where the condition is satisfied and forcing the opponent to abandon this safe position, to lose "balance." In this particular game, symmetry with respect to the center of the table comes to mind as a useful invariant. The first player can establish symmetry by placing the first coin at the center of the table. On subsequent moves, the first player always picks the same size coin as the opponent and places it symmetrically to the one just placed by the second player. The first player always maintains the symmetry of the configuration with respect to the center of the table, an invariant. The second player is always forced to break the symmetry. At the end, the first player places a coin in the last remaining spot.

In computer science, the concept of invariant applies to loops. A condition that is related to the purpose of the computation and holds true before the loop and after each iteration through the loop is called a *loop invariant*. Loop invariants are useful for reasoning about the code and for formally proving its correctness.

Example 3

The code below (from Figure 2-2 on Page 25) has one loop:

```
def sum1ToN(n):
    "returns 1 + 2 + ... + n"
    s = 0
    k = 1
    while k <= n:
        s += k # add k to s
        k += 1 # increment k by 1
    return s
```

Find a loop invariant for that loop.

Solution

The purpose of the loop is to calculate $1+2+...+n$. Before the loop, $s=0$ and $k=1$. After the last iteration through the loop, $k=n+1$ and $s=1+2+...+n$. The loop invariant here is $s=1+2+...+(k-1)$.

Exercises

1.   A domino covers exactly two squares on a chessboard, so it is possible to cover the board with 32 dominos. Now suppose we cut out the two white squares at the opposite corners of the board. Try to cover the remaining 62 squares with 31 dominos. Is it possible? If not, explain why not. ✓

2.   In chess a knight moves by two squares in one direction, then by one square in a perpendicular direction. Is it possible for a knight to visit each square exactly once and return to the starting position? If yes, show an example; if not, explain why not. Is it possible on a 7-by-7 "chessboard"?

3.▪   Consider a rectangle $AOBC$ on the coordinate plane, such that O is the origin, AO is on the x-axis, OB is on the y-axis, and C is in the first quadrant. Describe the locus of points (that is the set of all points) C, such that the perimeter of the rectangle is equal to p, a constant.

4.■   Consider a rectangle $AOBC$ in the first quadrant on the coordinate plane, such that O is the origin, and C moves along a branch of the hyperbola $y = \dfrac{1}{x}$. Describe an invariant property of the rectangle (beyond the obvious fact that O stays at the origin). ✓

5.■   Demonstrate geometrically that among all the rectangles with a given area, the square has the smallest perimeter. ⸰ Hint: see Questions 3 and 4. ⸰ ✓

6.■   Several pluses and minuses are written in a line, for example: $+ - - - + + - - + + + -$. If the first two symbols at the beginning of the line are the same, you add a plus at the end; if they are different, you add a minus. Then you erase the first two symbols. The operation is repeated until only one plus or minus remains. Is the remaining symbol always the same, regardless of whether you have proceeded from left to right or from right to left?

7.■   Erin and Owen share a computer. They want to make a schedule for the exclusive use of the computer, from noon to midnight, and they have decided to turn this into a game. On each move, a player can reserve a contiguous block of available time, up to two hours, starting at any time. The players take turns making reservations. They have tossed a coin, and Erin goes first. Does Owen have a strategy that would allow him to get at least as much total time as Erin, no matter what she does?

8.◆   The table below lists the numbers of vertices, edges, and faces in four polyhedrons:

	Vertices	**Edges**	**Faces**
Tetrahedron	4	6	4
Cube	8	12	6
Triangular prism	6	9	5
Icosahedron	12	30	20

Describe an invariant that connects the number of vertices V, the number of edges E, and the number of faces F in a polyhedron. Show that this is indeed an invariant for all polyhedrons. In fact, the edges and faces do not have to be "straight:" the same invariant remains as long as the edges and faces do not intersect. ✓

9.   Identify a loop invariant for your solution to Question 6 in Section 4.5 (page 75).

10.4 Finite Strategy Games

Suppose a game has a finite number of possible positions. Two players take turns advancing from one position to the next, according to the rules of the game. Positions never repeat: a position that occurred once can never happen again. So sooner or later, when a *terminal* position is reached, the game ends. Depending on the rules, the player who made the last move wins or loses, while some of the terminal positions may be designated as ties. Alternatively, the players may collect some points along the way, and the player with the higher score wins. Games of this type are called *finite strategy games*. In some games, such as Nim, reaching a terminal position (taking the last stone) signifies a win, and there are no ties. We will discuss real Nim a little later; first, let us consider a very simple version.

Example 1

There is a pile of N stones. Two players take turns making moves. On each move, a player can take one, two, or three stones from the pile. The player who takes the last stone wins. Let's call this game Nim-1-3 (*nimm* is German for "take"). Does the first or the second player have a winning strategy? What is that strategy?

Solution

This game is equivalent to (a mathematician might say *isomorphic*, that is, "has the same form" as) the game where the players advance a token along a linear board from left to right; on each move a player can advance the token by one, two, or three squares:

The length of the board is $N+1$. The position on the board corresponds to the number of stones left in the pile; the first square corresponds to N stones, the last one to 0 stones in the pile. (It is often convenient to choose a model for the game, which is isomorphic to the original game, but is easier to visualize and work with.)

To solve this game, we will use a work-backwards method. Let us first mark the winning position with a plus sign:

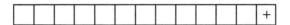

This position is safe: that's where you want to end up. Now let us find all the positions from which the plus position can be reached. These are unsafe for you: if you land there, your opponent can jump to a plus. Let us mark each of them with a minus sign:

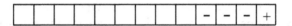

Now there is one position from which you can move only to a minus (unsafe position). This position is safe for you, so let's mark it with a plus:

Again let us find all the positions from where one can reach any plus position and mark them with minuses. Continuing this process, we will eventually mark up the whole board:

If the starting position is safe (marked with a plus), the first player is forced to abandon it, and the second player can win, moving to a safe position on every turn. In Nim-1-3 this happens when the initial number of stones $N = 4k$ (N is evenly divisible by four). If the starting position is unsafe (marked with a minus), then the first player can move to a safe position right away, and eventually win. In Nim-1-3 this happens when N is not evenly divisible by four.

We can represent all the positions in a finite game as points and each legal move as an arrow from one position to the next. As explained later, in Chapter 15, such a structure is called a *directed graph*. The fact that game positions never repeat means that the graph is *acyclic*; that is, it has no circular paths. Representing games as graphs is useful for developing the mathematical theory of finite games. A lot is known about graphs! But it is too cumbersome for analyzing a particular game, even as simple as Nim-1-3. It is better, instead to look for a simple enough property or formula that describes all the safe positions.

There is a simple formula for the safe positions in the Nim-1-3 game: it is safe to move to a position where the number of stones remaining in the pile is evenly divisible by 4. So there is no need to remember the chart of all safe positions; it is much easier to use the formula. Not every game, however, has a simple formula. Let us consider a more interesting game, for which a simple property or formula for safe positions hasn't been found yet.

Example 2

In the game of Chomp, the board represents a rectangular grid (like a bar of chocolate). Players take turns taking "bites" from the grid. A "bite" consists of one square plus all the squares to the right and/or below it. For example:

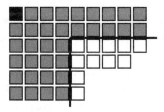

The square in the upper left corner is "poison"; the player who is forced to "eat" the poison loses the game.

It is possible, of course, to apply to Chomp the work-backwards method described in Example 1 and come up with a list of all safe positions (see Question 8 in the exercises). Such analysis, however, would be very tedious for larger boards if we tried doing it by hand. It is better to program a computer to do that. No one, so far, has been able to come up with a compact property or formula that describes all safe positions in Chomp, except for two special board sizes: n-by-2 and n-by-n (see Questions 6 and 7 in the exercises).

One peculiar thing about Chomp is that we can prove, even without knowing anything about any specific strategy, that the first player can always win (as long as the board is larger than 1 by 1). Here is a proof by contradiction. Suppose it is the second player who has a winning strategy. So he has a winning response to each of the first player's moves. If the first player "bites off" just one square, at the lower right corner, in his first move, the second player has a winning move in response. But the first player could have made that winning move first! This proof is based on the argument called *strategy stealing*: in this game the second player can't have a winning strategy because the first player would "steal" it.

Our last example in this section is the real game of Nim. In Nim there are several piles of stones. On each move, a player must take at least one stone but can take any number of stones from one pile. The player who takes the last stone wins. (There is another version of Nim in which the player who takes the last stone loses. The winning strategy in this take-last-and-lose Nim is similar to our Nim.)

Nim is sometimes presented as an arrangement of cards or tokens in several rows. For example:

Each row represents a pile of stones. Another isomorphic model for Nim is several tokens on a rectangular board moving in the same direction. For example:

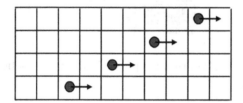

Each token's distance from the rightmost square represents the number of stones in the corresponding pile.

It is possible to use the work-backwards method to determine a strategy for Nim. This is not very interesting, though, and quite tedious when the numbers are large. Luckily, Nim has a very elegant description of the winning strategy based on an interesting property of its safe positions.

Suppose N_1, N_2, ..., N_k are the numbers of stones left in the piles. The idea is for the winning player to always maintain some kind of "balance" among these numbers. The losing player is forced to change one of the numbers and break the balance; then the winning player restores the balance again. But what kind of balance? Perhaps some kind of checksum might work. When one of the numbers changes, the checksum will change, too. The problem is, the winning player must be able to restore the checksum by <u>reducing</u> one of the numbers. Conventional checksum algorithms don't work like that. We need something more ingenious.

Let us arrange the binary representations of N_1, N_2, ..., N_k in one vertical column, with the rightmost digits aligned. For example, if the numbers are 1, 3, 5, and 7, we get

N_1	1
N_2	11
N_3	101
N_4	111

Now consider the parity of each column — whether the number of 1s in the column is even or odd. In the final winning position, all the numbers are zeros, so the parity of all the columns is even. Let us declare safe all positions with this property: the parity of all columns is even. All other positions are unsafe.

The parities of the columns can be considered as binary digits of a kind of "checksum." Calculating this "checksum" is equivalent to performing bit-wise addition, or — same thing — the bit-wise XOR (exclusive OR) operation on the numbers (see Section 7.3). This "checksum" is called the *Nim sum*. In safe positions the Nim sum must be 0. For example:

	Safe:		*Unsafe:*
N_1	1	N_1	1
N_2	11	N_2	1
N_3	101	N_3	101
N_4	111	N_4	111
	===		===
Nim sum	000		010

It is very easy to calculate the Nim sum on a computer (see Question 10).

From a safe position you are forced to move to an unsafe one. Indeed, when a player takes one or several stones from the j-th pile, N_j changes, so at least one of its binary digits changes. The parity of the column that holds that digit will change, too. For example, in the 1-3-5-7 configuration, the numbers of bits in the three columns are 2, 2, and 4 — all even, so this is a safe position. The first player is forced to abandon it on the first move, so the second player can win.

Is it true, though, that from any unsafe position you can always move to a safe one? In other words, is it true that the even-parity-of-all-columns property can always be restored by <u>reducing</u> one of the numbers? The answer is yes, and here is why. Suppose some of the columns have odd parity. Let's take the leftmost of them. Since its parity is odd, it must have at least one bit in it set to 1. Let's take the row that contains that bit and flip (from 1 to 0 or from 0 to 1) all the bits in that row that are in odd-parity columns. The even parity of all columns will be restored. The new number represented by the row will be smaller than the original number, because the leftmost flipped bit (that is, the leftmost binary digit flipped) has changed from 1 to 0.

For example, suppose in the 1-3-5-7 configuration, the first player removes the entire second pile. The numbers become 1, 0, 5, 7:

N_1	1
N_2	0
N_3	101
N_4	111
	===
Nim sum	011

The parity of the second and third columns becomes odd. The second column is the leftmost among them. The bit in the fourth row is set to 1. Let's take that row and flip the bits in it that are in the odd-parity columns. (This is equivalent to XOR-ing that row with the Nim sum.) We get:

N_1	1
N_2	0
N_3	101
N_4	100
	===
Nim sum	000

The even parity of all columns is restored: the Nim sum is 0 again. N_4 becomes 4. So to restore the balance and return to a safe position from the 1-0-5-7 position, the second player should take from the fourth pile 3 stones out of 7, leaving 4 stones.

Nim is important, because there are many more general versions of it (see, for example, Question 12 in the exercises), and many games are isomorphic to a version of Nim.

Exercises

1.   What property describes the safe positions in the Nim-1-4 game, in which you have one pile of stones and are allowed to take 1, 2, 3, or 4, stones on each move? ✓

2.   Write a Python program that plays Nim-1-3.

3.   In this game, two players take turns moving a token on an 8-by-8 board. At the beginning, the token is placed in the lower left corner. On each move, the token can be moved by one square up or to the right or diagonally up and to the right:

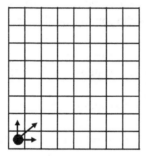

The player who reaches the upper right corner first wins. Find all safe positions in this game. Can the first player always win? ✓

4.   Describe an isomorphic version of the game from Question 3, as a game that uses piles of stones instead of the board. Describe the safe positions in your version. ✓

5.■   Suppose the game from Question 3 has been modified: now the field has a poisonous swamp, like this:

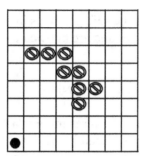

The player who has no valid move or is forced into the swamp loses. Find all safe positions on the above board and show that the first player can win. If the first player moves diagonally on the first move, what is the correct response?

6.   Come up with the winning strategy for Chomp with an *n*-by-2 board.

7.■   Come up with the winning strategy for Chomp with an *n*-by-*n* board.

8.♦   Use the work-backwards method to find all safe positions in 4-by-3 Chomp. What is the winning first move in this game? ✓

9.   Is the Nim position with four piles of 3, 4, 5, and 6 stones safe?

10.   Write and test a Python function that takes a Nim position, represented as a list of non-negative integers, and checks whether it is safe.

11.   What is the correct move in Nim if three piles are left with 6, 8, and 11 stones in them? ✓

12.♦   Consider the following modified version of Nim. In this game, stacks of coins are placed on some of the squares of a one-dimensional board:

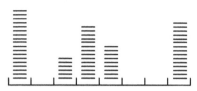

On his move, a player can take several coins (at least one) from any stack and add them to the next stack to the right (or start a new stack there, if that square was empty). Players are not allowed to take coins from the rightmost stack. Whoever moves the last coin wins. Describe the safe positions in this game.

13.♦   Six stacks of coins are arranged in a line on the table:

Two players take turns taking coins: on his move a player must take the whole stack of coins, either on the left or on the right end. The player who ends up with most coins wins. Come up with a strategy for the first player that assures that he collects at least as many coins as his opponent. ⸮ Hint: imagine that the stacks are arranged on a chessboard, on squares of alternating colors. ⸞ ✓

14.■   In this game there are nine cards with the numbers 1 through 9 written on them. Two players take turns, taking one card on each turn. The player who is first to collect three cards with numbers that add up to 15 wins. If the first player takes 5, is 3 or 4 the correct response? Come up with a strategy that assures a win or a tie for the first player. ⸮ Hint: imagine that the cards are arranged on the table and form a 3-by-3 magic square (the sums of the numbers in each row, each column, and each of the two diagonals are the same); instead of picking up a card, the player writes his initials on it. ⸞

10.5 Review

Terms introduced in this chapter:

> *Redundancy*
> *Parity*
> *Checksum*
> *Check digit*
> *Substitution error*
> *Transposition error*
> *Invariant*
> *Loop invariant*
> *Finite strategy game*
> *Safe and unsafe positions*
> *Strategy stealing*
> *Nim*
> *Nim sum*

11 Recurrence Relations and Recursion

11.1 Prologue

In Chapter 1 we talked about different ways to define a function: in words, with a table, with a chart, or with a formula. But we left out one very important method: we can also describe a function, especially a function on positive (or non-negative) integers, *recursively*. Here is an example. Suppose you state that a function f with the domain of all positive integers is defined as follows:

$$f(n) = \begin{cases} 1, \text{ if } n = 1 \\ n \cdot f(n-1), \text{ if } n > 1 \end{cases}$$

This definition does not tell us right away how to find the value of $f(n)$. $f(n)$ is described in terms of $f(n-1)$ (except for one simple *base case*, $n = 1$). And yet, with some work, we can find the value of $f(n)$ for any positive n. Let's see: we know that $f(1) = 1$. Next: $f(2) = 2 \cdot f(1) = 2 \cdot 1 = 2$. Next: $f(3) = 3 \cdot f(2) = 3 \cdot 2 = 6$. Next: $f(4) = 4 \cdot f(3) = 4 \cdot 6 = 24$. And so on. There is only one function that satisfies the above definition. In this case you can easily find a formula to describe this function: it is our old friend $f(n) = n!$ (*n*-factorial).

Recursion is a powerful tool for defining functions. The designers of computer hardware and programming languages have made sure that recursion is also supported in programming languages.

11.2 Recurrence Relations

Recall that a function defined on the set of all positive integers can be expressed as a sequence of the function's values: $a_1, a_2, ..., a_n, ...$ To define such a function recursively, we define each term of the sequence, except the first (or, perhaps, the first few), through its relation to the previous term(s). The relation that connects the *n*-th term to one or more of the previous terms is often the same for each *n*. It is called a *recurrence relation*. For example:

$$\begin{cases} a_1 = 1 \\ a_n = na_{n-1}, \text{ for any } n \geq 2 \end{cases}$$

We get, again, $a_n = n!$. This is the same as our recursive definition of *n*!, just rewritten in a slightly different way.

It is easy to calculate on a computer the values of a sequence defined through a recurrence relation. Recall, for example, our calculation of $s(n) = 1 + 2 + ... + n$ in Chapter 4. We noticed that $s(0) = 0$ and $s(n) = s(n-1) + n$, for any $n \geq 2$. This led to the following Python code:

```
n = 1
sum1n = 0
while n <= nMax:
    sum1n += n
    print('{0:3d} {1:6d}'.format(n, sum1n))
    n += 1
```

Here `sum1n` stands for $s(n)$. Iterations through the `while` loop are equivalent to calculating successive values of $s(n)$.

❖   ❖   ❖

One of the famous sequences defined with a recurrence relation is called *Fibonacci numbers*:

$$f_1 = 1; \; f_2 = 1$$
$$f_n = f_{n-1} + f_{n-2}, \text{ if } n > 2.$$

This sequence is named after Leonardo Fibonacci (the name means son of Bonaccio) who lived in Pisa in the 13th century, but the numbers were known in India over 2000 years ago. Fibonacci came upon the numbers while he was modeling a population of rabbits under simplistic assumptions: we start with one adult pair; an adult pair produces a pair of baby rabbits each month; a baby rabbit becomes an adult after one month; the rabbits never die. This model results in the Fibonacci recurrence relation for the number of adult pairs after *n* months (Figure 11-1). The sequence goes like this: 1, 1, 2, 3, 5, 8, 13, 21, 34, and so on. f_n represents the number of adult pairs of rabbits at month *n*. The total number of pairs of rabbits — adults and babies — is also a Fibonacci sequence, but it starts at $p_1 = 1$; $p_2 = 2$, $p_n = p_{n-1} + p_{n-2}$, if $n > 2$.

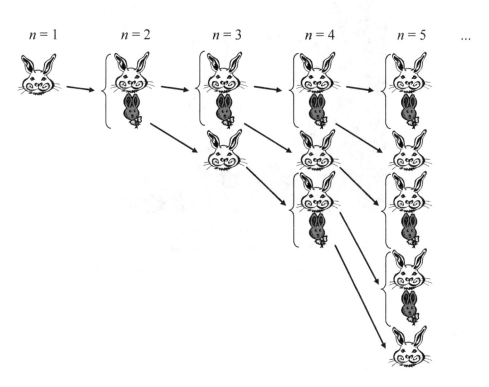

Figure 11-1. Rabbits' population growth in the Fibonacci model.

— **adult pair**   — **baby pair**

Fibonacci numbers have many interesting properties. For example, the sequence of ratios of consecutive Fibonacci numbers $r_n = \dfrac{f_{n+1}}{f_n}$ converges to the *golden ratio* $\tau = \dfrac{1 + \sqrt{5}}{2} \approx 1.62$. Fibonacci numbers pop up in various branches of mathematics and in the natural world (Figure 11-2; search the Internet for "fibonacci + nature" for other examples).

**Figure 11-2.   Broccoli Romanesco.   The numbers of clusters in
the spirals form Fibonacci sequences.**

Photograph by Madelaine Zadik, courtesy Botanic Garden of Smith College.

Exercises

1.   Consider a function

$$f(n) = \begin{cases} 1, \text{ if } n = 1 \\ 2 \cdot f(n-1) + 1, \text{ if } n > 1 \end{cases}$$

What is $f(4)$? ✓

2.   A function on positive integers is described by

$$f(n) = \begin{cases} 1, \text{ if } n = 1 \\ f(n-1) + 2, \text{ if } n > 1 \end{cases}$$

Redefine it by a simple non-recursive formula.

3.   Define $f(n) = 2^n$ recursively, in terms of $f(n-1)$, for all integers $n \geq 1$. ✓

4. ▪ Write a recursive definition of a function $f(n)$ that has the following properties: $f(1) = 10$, $f(2) = 30$, and the values $f(1)$, $f(2)$, ..., $f(n)$, ... form an arithmetic sequence. ✓

5. ▪ The same as Question 4, but for a geometric sequence.

6. ▪ Describe the function from Question 1 with a simple formula, without recursion.

7. ▪ Define recursively, without factorials, the function $f(n) = \dfrac{n!}{(n-3)!}$ for integers $n \geq 3$. ✓

8. Given $a_1 = 1$, $a_n = a_{n-1} + n$ for any $n \geq 2$, describe a_n with a simple non-recursive formula in terms of n.

9. ▪ Write a Python program that prompts the user to enter a positive integer n and prints the first n Fibonacci numbers.

10. ◆ Find a sequence that satisfies the Fibonacci equation $a_n = a_{n-1} + a_{n-2}$, if $n > 2$ and, at the same time, is a geometric sequence with $a_1 = 1$. How many such sequences are there?

11.3 Recursion in Programs

Now back to our favorite, $s(n) = 1 + 2 + ... + n$. As we have seen, the recursive definition of $s(n)$ is $s(n) = \begin{cases} 1, \text{ if } n = 1 \\ s(n-1) + n, \text{ if } n > 1 \end{cases}$. Now suppose, just out of curiosity, we implement this definition directly in a Python function:

```
def sum1toN(n):
    if n == 1:
        return 1
    else:
        return sum1toN(n-1) + n
```

Will this work? What will `sum1toN(5)` return? As you know, in a program, a function translates into a piece of code that is callable from different places in the program. The caller passes to the function some argument values and a return address — the address of the instruction to which to return control after the function finishes its work. So how can this work when a piece of code passes control to itself? Won't the program get confused? Won't Python choke trying to swallow its own tail?

And yet it works! Try it:

```
>>> sum1toN(5)
15
```

Because recursion is such a useful tool in programming, the developers of Python (and other programming languages) have made special efforts to ensure it works. There are also CPU instructions that facilitate implementing recursive calls.

Here is an allegory for what happens. Imagine a function as a mail-order bakery. To place an order you take an empty box, put your written order into it and also put in a label with your address, and ship it to the bakery. The baker, call him Frank, receives the box, reads the order (the arguments you pass to the function), bakes the cake you ordered, puts it in the box, attaches your label, and ships the box back to you.

Now suppose Frank has received an order and is working on it. Meanwhile a new order arrives. Frank immediately drops what he is doing, saves the unfinished cake (the values of the local variables) in the box the order came in, then puts the new box that has just arrived <u>on top</u> of the one he was working on, opens the new box, and starts working on that. Meanwhile a new order arrives. Frank immediately drops what he is doing, saves the unfinished cake (the values of the local variables) in the box the order came in, then puts the new box that has just arrived <u>on top</u> of the one he was working on, opens the new box, and starts working on that. Meanwhile... You get the picture. The orders keep coming and the boxes keep piling up: now there is a whole *stack* of them.

Finally, at some point, Frank gets a break: the orders stop coming. Frank finishes the top order and ships it to the customer. He then finishes the one that was just below it and ships that to the customer. And so on, until he gets to the bottom of the stack, to the last remaining order, finishes that order, and goes home.

You might be wondering: Why is Frank processing orders in this funny sequence? The order that came in last is completed first. Wouldn't it be more fair to do it in a first-in-first-out manner? In a moment you will see why Frank does it his way.

One day, Frank received an order for a multi-layered wedding cake with four layers. The layers in such a cake are basically the same, only each layer is smaller in diameter than the one beneath it. Frank started working on the bottom layer, but began to worry that he'd get confused in all the layers. Luckily, a friend of his (a computer programmer) came up with this fabulous idea: why doesn't Frank send an order to himself for a multi-layered cake that consists of the three top layers, and then, when the three-layer cake is ready, just put it on top of the layer he is working on? Frank doesn't have to ship his order very far, of course, but he still follows his usual procedure: takes an empty box, writes out an order for a three-layer cake, writes a label with the return address (his own) and sends in the order (by putting the box on the top of the stack). Then as usual, he opens the box and sees: aha, an order for a three-layer cake! So he writes himself an order for a two-layer cake. You get the picture. Finally Frank receives (his own) order for a single-layer cake. He finishes it quickly and ships it back (to himself, of course). He receives it, uses it to complete the two-layer cake, and ships that back (to himself). Receives it, completes the three-layer cake, ships back, receives that, completes the four-layer cake, and finally ships it to the customer. Due to his LIFO (last-in-first-out) method, Frank untangles the whole layered business without any confusion.

This seems like a lot of shipping back and forth, but it is easy for a computer. Python allocates a special chunk of memory, called a *stack*, for recursive function calls. The CPU has the `push` instruction that puts a data item onto the top of the stack. The complementary `pop` instruction removes and returns the top item.

In Python, Frank's activity may be represented as something like this (assuming the + operator is properly defined for cakes):

```
def bakeSingleLayeredCake(d):
    'Bakes a simple cake of diameter d'
    return Cake(d)

def bakeMultiLayeredCake(n):
    'Bakes a cake with n layers'
    d = 3 * n  # the diameter of the bottom layer in inches
    cake = bakeSingleLayeredCake(d)
    # Base case: n == 1 -- do nothing
    # Recursive case:
    if n > 1:
        cake += bakeMultiLayeredCake(n - 1)
    return cake
```

For a recursive function to work, it must have a simple *base case*, where recursive calls are not needed.

In the above code, n == 1 is the base case.

> **When a function is called recursively, it must be called for smaller and smaller tasks, which eventually converge to the base case (or one of the base cases).**

Each time we call the function bakeMultiLayeredCake(n-1) recursively, we call it with an argument that is smaller by 1 than the previous time.

Recursion has its cost: first, you need to have enough space on the stack and, second, the code spends extra time pushing and popping data and calling the same function. Iterations are often more efficient. But some applications, especially those dealing with nested structures or branching processes, require a stack anyway, and recursion allows you to write very concise and clear code.

Example 1

Write a recursive function that calculates 10^n for a non-negative integer n.

Solution

```
def pow10(n):
    if n == 0:  # base case
        return 1
    else:
        return pow10(n-1) * 10
```

Example 2

Write a recursive function that returns the sum of the digits in a non-negative integer.

Solution

```
def sumDigits(n):
    s = n % 10
    # Base case: n < 10 -- do nothing
    # Recursive case:
    if n >= 10:
        s += sumDigits(n // 10)
    return s
```

Example 3

Write a recursive function that takes a string and returns a reversed string.

Solution

```
def reverse(s):
    if len(s) > 1:
        s = reverse(s[1:]) + s[0]
    return s
```

The base case here is implicit: when the string is empty or consists of only one character, there is nothing to do.

❖   ❖   ❖

A very popular example of recursion in computer programming books and tutorials is the "Towers of Hanoi" puzzle. We have three pegs and n disks of increasing size. Initially all the disks are stacked in a tower on one of the pegs (Figure 11-3). The objective is to move the tower to another peg, one disk at a time, without ever placing a bigger disk on top of a smaller one.

Figure 11-3.   The Towers of Hanoi puzzle

The key to the solution is to notice that in order to move the whole tower, we first need to move a smaller tower of $n-1$ disks to the spare peg, then move the bottom disk to the destination peg, then move the tower of $n-1$ disks from the spare peg to the destination peg (Figure 11-4).

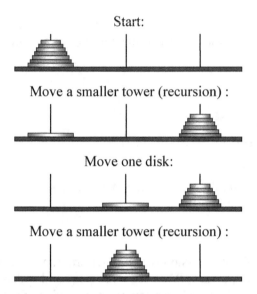

Figure 11-4. A recursive solution to Towers of Hanoi

Example 4

Write a recursive function that solves the Towers of Hanoi puzzle for *n* disks.

Solution

```
def moveTower(nDisks, fromPeg, toPeg):
    sparePeg = 6 - fromPeg - toPeg
    if nDisks > 1:
        moveTower(nDisks - 1, fromPeg, sparePeg)

    print('From ' + str(fromPeg) + ' to ' + str(toPeg))
    # This code does not model disk movements
    # -- it just prints out each move

    if nDisks > 1:
        moveTower(nDisks - 1, sparePeg, toPeg)
```

If we want to move a tower of, say, seven disks from peg 1 to peg 2, an initial call to moveTower would be moveTower(7, 1, 2).

Note that in the above example the function does not return a value (more precisely, it returns None), so it is a *recursive procedure*. Programming this task without recursion would be rather difficult.

Exercises

1. Write and test a recursive function that returns *n*!. Do not use any loops. ✓

2. In Section 5.3 Question 7, you created a function intToBin(n) that takes a non-negative integer and returns a string of its binary digits. For example, intToBin(5) returns '101'. Rewrite this function recursively, without any loops. ⸨ Hint: implement two base cases: n == 0 and n == 1: they cover the situations when n has only one binary digit. ⸩

3. Write and test a function

    ```
    def printDigits(n):
    ```

    that displays a triangle with *n* rows, made of digits. For example, printDigits(5) should display

    ```
    55555
    4444
    333
    22
    1
    ```

    The function's code under the def line should be three lines. ⸨ Hint: print n*str(n) prints '*n*' *n* times. ⸩ ✓

4. The same as Question 3, but invert the triangle, so that printDigits(5) prints

    ```
    1
    22
    333
    4444
    55555
    ```

5. Explain the statement sparePeg = 6 - fromPeg - toPeg in Example 4. ✓

6. Identify the base case in the `moveTower` function in Example 4. ✓

7. Without running the code in Example 4, determine the output when `moveTower(3, 1, 2)` is called.

8. The Towers of Hanoi puzzle was invented by the French mathematician Edouard Lucas in 1883. The "legend" that accompanied the puzzle stated that in Benares, India, there was a temple with a dome that marked the center of the world. The Hindu priests in the temple moved golden disks between three diamond needles. God placed 64 gold disks on one needle at the time of creation and the universe will come to an end when the priests have moved all 64 disks to another needle. What is the total number of moves needed to move a tower of 2 disks? 3 disks? 4 disks? n disks? Assuming one move per second, estimate the lifespan of the universe. ✓

11.4 Mathematical Induction

Let d_n be the number of moves required to move a tower of n disks in the Towers of Hanoi puzzle. It is pretty obvious that, for $n>1$, $d_n = d_{n-1} + 1 + d_{n-1} = 2d_{n-1} + 1$, because to move a tower of n disks, we need to first move a tower of $n-1$ disks, then one disk, then again a tower of $n-1$ disks. If you finished the last exercise, you probably guessed correctly that $d_n = 2^n - 1$. How can we prove this fact more rigorously? In questions of this kind we can use the method of proof called *mathematical induction*.

Suppose you have two sequences, $\{a_n\}$ and $\{b_n\}$. Suppose that:

1. $a_1 = b_1$ (base case).

2. For <u>any</u> $n>1$ you have managed to establish the following fact: <u>if</u> $a_{n-1} = b_{n-1}$ <u>then</u> $a_n = b_n$.

Is it true then that $a_n = b_n$ for all $n \geq 1$?

Let's see: we know that $a_1 = b_1$. We know that if $a_1 = b_1$ then $a_2 = b_2$. So we must have $a_2 = b_2$. Next step: we know that $a_2 = b_2$. We know that if $a_2 = b_2$ then $a_3 = b_3$. So we must have $a_3 = b_3$. Next step: ... and so on. We have to conclude that $a_n = b_n$ for all $n \geq 1$. In the future, we do not have to repeat this chain of reasoning steps every time — we just say our conclusion is true "by mathematical induction."

Example 1

Prove that the number of moves in the Towers of Hanoi puzzle for n disks $d_n = 2^n - 1$.

Solution

d_n satisfies the relationship

$$d_1 = 1,$$
$$d_n = 2d_{n-1} + 1 \text{ for } n > 1$$

We want to show that $d_n = 2^n - 1$ for all $n \geq 1$.

1. First let's establish the base case, $n = 1$. $d_1 = 1$ and $2^1 - 1 = 1$, so $d_1 = 2^1 - 1$. OK.

2. Now let's proceed with the *induction step*. <u>Assume</u> that $d_{n-1} = 2^{n-1} - 1$. Then $d_n = 2d_{n-1} + 1 = 2(2^{n-1} - 1) + 1 = 2^n - 2 + 1 = 2^n - 1$. So, for any $n > 1$, we were able to show that <u>if</u> $d_{n-1} = 2^{n-1} - 1$ <u>then</u> $d_n = 2^n - 1$.

By mathematical induction, $d_n = 2^n - 1$ for all $n \geq 1$, Q.E.D.

The method of mathematical induction applies to any sequence of propositions $\{P_n\}$. Suppose we know that P_1 is true; suppose we can show for any $n > 1$ that <u>if</u> P_{n-1} is true <u>then</u> P_n is true. Then, by mathematical induction, P_n is true for all $n \geq 1$. (In the above example, P_n is the proposition that $d_n = 2^n - 1$.)

Sometimes it is necessary to use a more general version of mathematical induction, with several base cases and a more general induction step. Suppose that:

1. $P_1, ..., P_k$ are true (base case(s)).

2. For any $n > k$ we can prove that <u>if</u> $P_1, P_2, ..., P_{n-1}$ are all true, <u>then</u> P_n is true.

Then, by mathematical induction, P_n is true for all $n \geq 1$.

Example 2

Prove that the n-th Fibonacci number $f_n \geq \left(\dfrac{3}{2}\right)^{n-2}$.

Solution

1. We can establish two base cases:

$$f_1 = 1 \geq \frac{2}{3} = \left(\frac{3}{2}\right)^{-1} = \left(\frac{3}{2}\right)^{1-2}$$

$$f_2 = 1 \geq \left(\frac{3}{2}\right)^0 = \left(\frac{3}{2}\right)^{2-2}.$$

2. Now the induction step. Assume that for any $m < n$ $f_m \geq \left(\dfrac{3}{2}\right)^{m-2}$. In

particular, for $n > 2$, $f_{n-1} \geq \left(\dfrac{3}{2}\right)^{n-3}$ and $f_{n-2} \geq \left(\dfrac{3}{2}\right)^{n-4}$. Then

$$f_n = f_{n-1} + f_{n-2} \geq \left(\frac{3}{2}\right)^{n-3} + \left(\frac{3}{2}\right)^{n-4} = \left(\frac{3}{2}\right)^{n-4}\left(\frac{3}{2}+1\right) =$$

$$\left(\frac{3}{2}\right)^{n-4} \cdot \frac{5}{2} > \left(\frac{3}{2}\right)^{n-4} \cdot \frac{9}{4} = \left(\frac{3}{2}\right)^{n-2}$$

So the proposition is true for the two base cases, and <u>if</u> it is true for $n-1$ and $n-2$ <u>then</u> it is also true for n. By math induction, it is true for all $n \geq 1$, Q.E.D.

If you finished Question 9 from Section 11.2, you probably tried to print the first 100 Fibonacci numbers and got $f_{100} = 354224848179261915075$. The above result explains why Fibonacci numbers grow so fast.

Exercises

1. Prove using mathematical induction that $1 + 3 + 5 + ... + (2n-1) = n^2$. ✓

2.■ Consider the following function:

```
def tangle(s):
    n = len(s)
    if n < 2:
        return ''   # empty string
    else:
        return tangle(s[1:n]) + s[1:n-1] + tangle(s[0:n-1])
```

Show that `tangle('abcde')` returns a string that contains neither `'a'` nor `'e'`.

3.◆ Show that for a string `s` of length n, `tangle(s)`, defined in Question 2, returns a string of length $L_n = 2^{n-1} - n$. ⋜ Hint: first obtain a recurrence relation for L_n, then prove it using mathematical induction. ⋝

4.◆ Suppose you have n straight lines in a plane, such that no two lines are parallel to each other and no three lines go through the same point. Show that the number of regions into which these lines cut the plane depends only on n, but not on a particular configuration of the lines. Find a formula for that number and prove it using mathematical induction. ⋜ Hint: when you add a line, the existing lines cut it into pieces. Each of these pieces cuts a region into two, adding a new region. ⋝ ✓

5.◆ Consider the sequence $a_0 = 2$, $a_1 = 2$, $a_n = 2a_{n-1} + 3a_{n-2}$ for $n \geq 2$. Write a Python program that prints out the first n terms of this sequence. Examine the pattern and come up with a non-recursive formula for a_n, then prove that your guess is correct using mathematical induction. ⋜ Hint: compare a_n to 3^n. ⋝

6.♦   Consider a recursive version of the function that returns the *n*-th Fibonacci number:

```
def fibonacci(n):
    if n == 1 or n == 2:
        return 1
    else:
        return fibonacci(n-1) + fibonacci(n-2)
```

Test it with $n = 6$ and $n = 20$. Now test it with $n = 100$. The computer won't return the result right away. Perhaps the recursive version takes a little longer... Prove by mathematical induction that the total number of calls to `fibonacci`, including the original call and all the recursive calls combined, is not less than the *n*-th Fibonacci number f_n. We have shown above that

$f_n \geq \left(\dfrac{3}{2}\right)^{n-2}$. Assuming that your computer can execute one trillion calls per

second, estimate how long you will have to wait for `fibonacci(100)` (in years). Press Ctrl-C to abort the program. As we said earlier, sometimes recursion can be costly.

11.5   Review

Terms introduced in this chapter:

> *Recurrence relation*
> *Fibonacci numbers*
> *Golden ratio*
> *Recursion*
> *Recursive function*
> *Recursive procedure*
> *Base case*
> *Mathematical induction*

Python feature introduced in this chapter:

> Recursive functions

12 Polynomials

12.1 Prologue

An expression

$$a_n x^n + a_{n-1} x^{n-1} + \ldots + a_1 x + a_0$$

is called a *polynomial*. The numbers a_n, a_{n-1}, ..., a_0 are called the *coefficients* of the polynomial. $a_n \neq 0$ is the *leading coefficient*; a_0 is called the *constant term*. n is called the *degree of the polynomial*. We will work with polynomials whose coefficients are real numbers. For example, an expression $2.4x^3 + 3x^2 + 1.5x + 4.9$ is a polynomial of degree 3, with the leading coefficient 2.4 and the constant term 4.9.

When we write polynomials, we usually omit the terms with zero coefficients. For example, $4x^2 + 0x + 1$ is written simply as $4x^2 + 1$. Also, when the coefficient is 1 we do not write it. For example, $1x^2 + 1x + 1$ is written simply as $x^2 + x + 1$. When a polynomial has a term with a negative coefficient, that coefficient is usually written with a minus sign in place of plus and without parentheses. For example, $x^7 + (-3)x^2$ is written simply as $x^7 - 3x^2$.

In computer programs, a polynomial can be represented as a list of its coefficients. For example, in Python $1.8x^5 - 3x^2 + 2.35$ can be represented as `p = [1.8, 0, 0, -3, 0, 2.35]`. An *n*-th degree polynomial is represented by a list with $n+1$ elements.

There are two ways to look at polynomials. First, we can view a polynomial as a function $P(x)$ defined by the formula $P(x) = a_n x^n + a_{n-1} x^{n-1} + \ldots + a_1 x + a_0$. We can calculate the value of $P(x)$ for any real number x. Second, we can view polynomials as abstract algebraic objects. We can add, subtract, multiply, and factor polynomials. We can study properties of polynomials with integer, rational, or real coefficients. In many important ways, the algebraic properties of polynomials parallel some properties of integers. For example, any positive integer can be factored, or represented as a product of primes, and such a representation is unique. Similarly, any polynomial can be uniquely represented as a product of "prime" polynomials (give or take constant factors). For example, $x^3 - 1 = (x-1)(x^2 + x + 1)$.

$a_2x^2 + a_1x + a_0$ is a second-degree polynomial. It is also called a *quadratic polynomial* and it defines a *quadratic function*. The letters *a*, *b*, and *c* are often used for the coefficients when we deal with the general form of a quadratic polynomial:

$$ax^2 + bx + c$$

$ax + b$, a first-degree polynomial, is called a *linear polynomial*. The polynomial of zero degree is simply a constant. It is convenient to consider 0 as a polynomial of degree 0.

Polynomials are important in mathematics and computer technology because they can be used to approximate other functions and smooth curves. For example, in scalable ("TrueType") fonts on your computer, the contour of each character is composed of quadratic *splines* (pieces of quadratic curves). It is easy to compute a value of a polynomial for a given *x*. Polynomials also serve as interesting models in abstract algebra.

12.2   Addition and Subtraction

The sum of two polynomials is a polynomial.

$$\left(a_nx^n + ... + a_1x + a_0\right) + \left(b_nx^n + ... + b_1x + b_0\right) =$$
$$\left(a_n + b_n\right)x^n + ... + \left(a_1 + b_1\right)x + \left(a_0 + b_0\right)$$

In other words, to add two polynomials we simply add the respective coefficients. If the degree of one polynomial is lower than the degree of the other, the missing terms in the lower-degree polynomial are considered to have zero coefficients.

Example 1

$$(3x^3 + 2x^2 + 7x + 2) + (4x^2 + 3x + 6) = 3x^3 + 6x^2 + 10x + 8$$

$$
\begin{array}{r}
3x^3 + 2x^2 + 7x + 2 \\
+ 4x^2 + 3x + 6 \\
\hline
3x^3 + 6x^2 + 10x + 8
\end{array}
$$

It is important to combine properly the *like terms* (that is, the terms with the same degree of *x*) when adding two polynomials.

Example 2

$$(3x^3 + 2x^2 + 7x + 2) + (4x^2 + 1) = 3x^3 + 6x^2 + 7x + 3$$

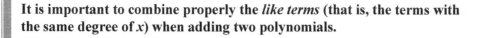

$$
\begin{array}{r}
3x^3 + 2x^2 + 7x + 2 \\
+\phantom{3x^3 + {}}4x^2 + 1 \\
\hline
3x^3 + 6x^2 + 7x + 3
\end{array}
$$

With a little practice, you can quickly learn to combine the like terms in your head and write the resulting sum without writing down the intermediate steps.

❖   ❖   ❖

When you combine the coefficients of the like terms of polynomials, pay careful attention to the signs.

Example 3

$$(3x^3 - 2x^2 - 7x + 2) + (4x^2 - 1) =$$
$$3x^3 + (-2 + 4)x^2 - 7x + (2 - 1) =$$
$$3x^3 + 2x^2 - 7x + 1$$

It is better to perform all the intermediate steps quickly in your head and write only the final result. Something like this: "for *x* cubed: 3 and nothing ==> $\boxed{3x^3}$; for *x* squared: $-2 + 4$ ==> $\boxed{+2x^2}$; for *x*: $-7 +$ nothing ==> $\boxed{-7x}$; for constant terms: $+2 - 1$ ==> $\boxed{+1}$."

❖   ❖   ❖

To negate a polynomial you need to negate all of its coefficients. $P_1 - P_2$ is the same as $P_1 + \left(-P_2\right)$.

Example 4

$$(x^2 - 1) - (2x^3 + x^2 - 5x + 1) =$$
$$(x^2 - 1) + (-2x^3 - x^2 + 5x - 1) =$$
$$-2x^3 + 5x - 2$$

With a little practice, you can learn to subtract a polynomial from another polynomial in your head and write only the final result.

Exercises

1.   Using a graphing calculator or a function plotting program from the Internet, plot on the same screen $y = \sin(x)$ and $y = x - \dfrac{x^3}{6}$. For which values of x does the polynomial $x - \dfrac{x^3}{6}$ give a reasonable approximation of $\sin(x)$?

2.   Simplify $\left(x^4 + 3x^2 + 1\right) + \left(x^3 + x^2 + 8\right)$. ✓

3.   Simplify $\left(2x^4 + x^3 + 4\right) - \left(x^4 + 2x^3 + 5\right)$.

4.   Simplify $\left(2.5x^4 - 1.2x^3 + 3\right) - \left(-2x^3 + 1\right)$.

5.   Write and test a Python function `negate(p)` that negates the polynomial represented by the list of its coefficients `p` and returns a new polynomial (represented as a list). ⸨ Hint: use a list comprehension. ⸩ ✓

6.   Write a Python function `evalPolynomial(p, x)` that returns the value of $P(x)$, where P is the polynomial represented by the list of its coefficients `p`. For example, `evalPolynomial([1, 0, 3], 2)` should return $1 \cdot 2^2 + 0 \cdot 2 + 3 = 7$. Use a single `while` loop. ⸨ Hint: keep track of x^k. ⸩

7.■   Write a recursive version of `evalPolynomial(p, x)`, based on the formula $a_n x^n + a_{n-1} x^{n-1} + \ldots + a_1 x + a_0 = x\left(a_n x^{n-1} + a_{n-1} x^{n-1} + \ldots + a_1\right) + a_0$. ✓

8.∎ Write a non-recursive version of `evalPolynomial(p, x)`, based on the formula $a_n x^n + a_{n-1} x^{n-1} + \ldots + a_1 x + a_0 = \left(\ldots \left(\left(a_n \right) x + a_{n-1} \right) x + \ldots + a_1 \right) x + a_0$.

Use one `while` loop. ⸮ Hint: start with $y = a_n$ and go from there: $y \leftarrow y \cdot x + a_{n-1}$, etc. ⸮

9.∎ Write and test a function `add(p1, p2)` that adds the polynomials `p1` and `p2` (represented as lists) and returns their sum (represented as a list). When you add or subtract polynomials, several leading coefficient(s) in the result may become zeros. Don't forget to get rid of them.

⸮ Hints:

1. The degree of the sum does not exceed the largest of the degrees of `p1` and `p2`.

2. Find the first non-zero element of the resulting list and return the slice of the list starting from that element.

⸮

10.◆ Write and test a Python function `toString(p)` that takes a polynomial with integer coefficients (represented as a list of its coefficients) and returns a string that represents the polynomial in the conventional form, as a sum of powers of x with appropriate coefficients. Use `"x^k"` to represent x^k. Test your function thoroughly on the following examples:

p	toString(p)
[1, 0, 0, 0, 0]	'x^4'
[3, 2, 1]	'3x^2 + 2x + 1'
[1, 0, 1]	'x^2 + 1'
[3, -2, 1]	'3x^2 - 2x + 1'
[-3, 0, 1]	'-3x^2 + 1'
[-1, 0, -1]	'-x^2 - 1'
[]	'0'
[0]	'0'
[0, 0, 0]	'0'

12.3   Multiplication, Division, and Roots

To multiply a polynomial by a number, we multiply each coefficient by that number. To multiply a polynomial by x^k, we add k to each exponent.

Example 1

$$\left(3x^3 - x^2 + 2x - 6\right) \cdot 3x^2 = 9x^5 - 3x^4 + 6x^3 - 18x^2$$

❖   ❖   ❖

If a polynomial is represented in a Python program as a list of its coefficients, then multiplication by x^k is equivalent to padding the list with k zeros at the end:

```
p = p + k*[0]
```

Example 2

$x^2 - 5x + 6$ is represented as `[1, -5, 6]`. What list represents $x^3 \cdot \left(x^2 - 5x + 6\right)$?

Solution

`[1, -5, 6, 0, 0, 0]`

To multiply a polynomial by another polynomial , we multiply each term of the first operand by each term of the second operand, then collect the like terms (with the appropriate signs).

Example 3

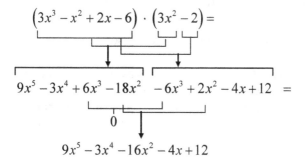

$$9x^5 - 3x^4 - 16x^2 - 4x + 12$$

The number of terms in the product, before collecting the like terms, is equal to the number of terms in the first polynomial times the number of terms in the second polynomial (here $4 \cdot 2 = 8$).

❖   ❖   ❖

Many algebra textbooks teach the so-called "FOIL" (First, Outer, Inner, Last) mnemonic rule for multiplying two linear polynomials. For example, $(2x-1)(3x+5) = 6x^2 + 10x - 3x - 5$. This order of listing the resulting terms works only for linear polynomials. It may mislead you when one or both factors are quadratics or polynomials of higher degrees. To find $P \cdot Q$, it is better to multiply each term of P by the first term of Q, then each term of P by the second term of Q, and so on. In the above example, we would get $(2x-1)(3x+5) = 6x^2 - 3x + 10x - 5$. This is not a big deal for linear polynomials — one can get used to either order — but it would be better if "FOIL" didn't exist, and you were taught the more general method from the outset. In either case, you have to collect the like terms at the end: $(2x-1)(3x+5) = 6x^2 - 3x + 10x - 5 = 6x^2 + 7x - 5$.

❖   ❖   ❖

Given two positive integers, we can divide one (the dividend) by the other (the divisor) and get a quotient and a remainder. For example, when we divide 17 by 3, the quotient is 5 and the remainder is 2: $17 = 5 \cdot 3 + 2$. The remainder is smaller then the divisor: $2 < 3$. A similar type of division with a remainder can be performed on polynomials with real coefficients. For example, if we divide $x^5 - 6.9x^4 + 5.3x^3 - 4x^2 + 3x + 1.2$ by $2x^2 - x + 0.2$, the quotient is $0.5x^3 - 3.2x^2 + x - 1.18$ and the remainder is $1.62x + 1.436$:

$$x^5 - 6.9x^4 + 5.3x^3 - 4x^2 + 3x + 1.2 =$$
$$\left(0.5x^3 - 3.2x^2 + x - 1.18\right)\left(2x^2 - x + 0.2\right) + \left(1.62x + 1.436\right)$$

The <u>degree</u> of the remainder is smaller than the <u>degree</u> of the divisor.

We can use the same *long division* algorithm for polynomials as we use for integers (Figure 12-1). As you can see, this can get quite tedious. Fortunately, CAS (Computer Algebra System) software and calculators can perform such tasks for you. Soon you will write your own Python function that implements the long division algorithm for polynomials (see Question 5).

$$
\begin{array}{r}
0.5x^3 - 3.2x^2 + x - 1.18 \\
2x^2 - x + 0.2 \overline{)\, x^5 - 6.9x^4 + 5.3x^3 - 4x^2 + 3x + 1.2} \\
\underline{x^5 - 0.5x^4 + 0.1x^3} \\
-6.4x^4 + 5.2x^3 - 4x^2 + 3x + 1.2 \\
\underline{-6.4x^4 + 3.2x^3 - 0.64x^2} \\
2x^3 - 3.36x^2 + 3x + 1.2 \\
\underline{2x^3 - x^2 + 0.2x} \\
-2.36x^2 + 2.8x + 1.2 \\
\underline{-2.36x^2 + 1.18x - 0.236} \\
1.62x + 1.436
\end{array}
$$

Figure 12-1. Example of long division for polynomials

❖   ❖   ❖

When you divide a polynomial by $(x-c)$, the remainder is a zero-degree polynomial, which is simply a constant:

$$P(x) = Q(x)(x-c) + r$$

r is the same for any x. It is easy to find the remainder r without division: if you plug c for x into the above equation, then $(x-c)$ becomes zero, and you get $P(c) = r$. This fact is known as the *remainder theorem*: $P(x) = Q(x)(x-c) + P(c)$.

A value of x such that $P(x) = 0$ is called a *root* (or a *zero*) of the polynomial $P(x)$.

> **To find all the roots of a polynomial is the same as to solve the equation** $P(x) = 0$.

As you know, a linear polynomial $ax + b$ has one root, $x = \dfrac{-b}{a}$. A quadratic polynomial $ax^2 + bx + c$ can have a maximum of two real roots: $x_1 = \dfrac{-b - \sqrt{b^2 - 4ac}}{2a}$ and $x_2 = \dfrac{-b + \sqrt{b^2 - 4ac}}{2a}$ (when $b^2 - 4ac \geq 0$). In general, an *n*-th degree polynomial with real coefficients can have up to n real roots.

The remainder theorem states that $P(x) = Q(x)(x - c) + P(c)$. In particular, $(x - c)$ evenly divides $P(x)$ if and only if $P(c) = 0$. This fact is a *corollary* to (follows directly from) the remainder theorem.

The above fact is also known as the *factor theorem*: c is a root of a polynomial $P(x)$ if and only if $(x - c)$ is a factor of $P(x)$. However, when we say "a factor of $P(x)$," we basically assume that a polynomial with real coefficients can be represented as a product of prime polynomial factors, and that such a representation is unique (up to constant factors). This is indeed true; moreover, the prime factors are all linear or quadratic polynomials. For example, $x^4 + 1 = (x^2 + \sqrt{2}x + 1)(x^2 - \sqrt{2}x + 1)$.

The proof is not easy, though; it uses *complex numbers* and follows from the *fundamental theorem of algebra*: any *n*-th degree polynomial ($n > 1$) with complex coefficients can be represented as a product of n linear factors (with complex coefficients) and, therefore, has exactly n complex roots (not necessarily all different). For example, $x^2 + 1 = (x - i)(x + i)$, where i is the *imaginary number* $i = \sqrt{-1}$. As for real roots, any <u>odd</u> degree polynomial with real coefficients has at least one real root.

> If $P(x)$ is an *n*-th degree polynomial $a_n x^n + ... + a_1 x + a_0$ with real
> coefficients and it has *n* roots $c_1, c_2, ..., c_n$, then
> $$P(x) = a_n(x - c_1)(x - c_2)...(x - c_n).$$

Exercises

1.   When solving an equation, it is often convenient to divide all the coefficients of a polynomial by the same number equal to the leading coefficient, so that the leading coefficient becomes 1. Write and test a function that does this. ⸬ Hint: it is easier to multiply the remaining coefficients by the reciprocal of the leading coefficient, then set the leading coefficient to 1. ⸬ ✓

2.   Write and test a function `multiplyByOneTerm(p, a, k)` that multiplies a given polynomial p, represented by a list of its coefficients, by ax^k and returns the product as a new list.

3.▪   Write and test a function `multiply(p1, p2)` that returns the product of two polynomials. Use one loop; within it, call `multiplyByOneTerm` from Question 2 and `add(p1, p2)` from Question 9 in Section 12.2.

4.▪   Write a version of `multiply(p1, p2)` that does not call other functions. Start with the result list of the appropriate length, filled with zeros, then calculate the value of each element of `result` as a sum of products:

```
result[0] = p1[0] * p2[0];
result[1] = p1[0] * p2[1] + p1[1] * p2[0];
```

and so on. ✓

5.◆   Write and test a function `divide(p1, p2)` that divides the polynomial p1 by the polynomial p2 and returns the quotient and the remainder (combined into a tuple). Use the long division algorithm.

6.▪   Write a version of `evalPolynomial(p, x)` that calculates the value of $P(x)$ using the `divide` function from Question 5 and the remainder theorem.

7.■   Write a program that prompts the user to enter a positive integer n and prints out the coefficients of the expansion of $(x+1)^n$ and their sum. ✓

8.■   One of the roots of the polynomial $P(x) = x^3 - 4x^2 - x + 12$ is 3. Find the other two roots. ≼ Hint: $(x-3)$ divides $P(x)$; use long division (or the Python function that you wrote in Question 5) to find the quotient. ≽

9.■   A quadratic polynomial $2x^2 + bx + c$ has the roots –2 and 6. Find b and c. ≼ Hint: Distribute $2(x - x_1)(x - x_2)$, where x_1 and x_2 are the roots of P, and compare the coefficients of the result to the coefficients of P. ≽

10.■   Given $x + y = p$, $xy = q$, find x and y in terms of p and q. ≼ Hint: write a quadratic equation such that x and y are its roots (see Question 9). ≽ ✓

12.4   Binomial Coefficients

If you expand $(x+1)^n$, you get a polynomial. What are its coefficients? You had a glimpse of them in Section 8.5, Question 8: the coefficient at x^k turns out to be $\binom{n}{k}$ (n-choose-k). In general, if you expand $(x+y)^n$, you get a sum of the terms $a_k x^k y^{n-k}$. Again, $a_k = \binom{n}{k}$. $(x+y)$ is a *binomial*, and the fact that the coefficients of $(x+y)^n$ are the numbers n-choose-k is called the *binomial theorem*.

The binomial theorem states that

$$(x+y)^n = \binom{n}{0}x^n + \binom{n}{1}x^{n-1}y + \ldots + \binom{n}{n}y^n = \sum_{k=0}^{n}\binom{n}{k}x^{n-k}y^k$$

That is why the n-choose-k numbers are often called *binomial coefficients*. The formula was discovered by Isaac Newton and announced by him in 1676.

The proof of the binomial theorem goes like this:

$$(x+y)^n = \underbrace{(x+y)\cdot(x+y)\cdot\ldots\cdot(x+y)}_{n}$$

When we distribute we form products of x's and y's:

$$\underbrace{x \cdot y \cdot x \cdot x \cdot \ldots \cdot y \cdot x}_{n} = x^{n-k} y^{k}$$

We pick from each set of parentheses either x or y and multiply them. When we collect the like terms, we get the coefficient for the term $x^{n-k} y^{k}$. So the question is how many ways are there to form $x^{n-k} y^{k}$. In order to get such a term we must take y k times and x $(n-k)$ times. So the coefficient is equal to the number of ways in which we can choose k objects (here the sets of parentheses where we picked y) from n (all sets of parentheses).

The fact that the n-choose-k numbers are also binomial coefficients is useful for establishing many of their amazing properties (see Questions 2 - 6).

Example 1

Expand $(x+y)^{4}$.

Solution

$$(x+y)^{4} = x^{4} + 4x^{3}y + 6x^{2}y^{2} + 4xy^{3} + y^{4}$$

Example 2

What is the coefficient at $x^{8}y^{10}$ in the expansion of $(x+y)^{18}$?

Solution

$$\binom{18}{10} = \frac{18!}{10! \cdot 8!} = 43758$$

It is very useful to remember the following identities, which, of course, are special cases of the binomial theorem:

$$(x+y)^2 = x^2 + 2xy + y^2 \qquad (x-y)^2 = x^2 - 2xy + y^2$$

$$(x+y)^3 = x^3 + 3x^2y + 3xy^2 + y^3 \qquad (x-y)^3 = x^3 - 3x^2y + 3xy^2 - y^3$$

❖ ❖ ❖

We can neatly arrange the n-choose-k numbers into a triangular table:

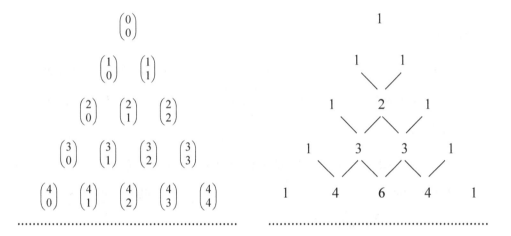

Now look at this triangle. It is symmetrical about its vertical axis. The numbers on the left and right borders are 1. Each number inside is the sum of the two numbers above it: $\binom{n}{k} = \binom{n-1}{k-1} + \binom{n-1}{k}$. Starting from the top, we can build as many rows of the triangle as we need.

This triangular table is known as *Pascal's Triangle* in honor of the French mathematician and philosopher Blaise Pascal (1623-1662). According to a brief historical note in Donald Knuth's *The Art of Computer Programming*, Pascal published the table in 1653 in his *Traité du Triangle Arithmétique*. This was one of the first works on probability theory. However, Pascal was not the first to describe the n-choose-k numbers or the triangle. According to Knuth, the triangle appeared in the treatise "The Precious Mirror of the Four Elements" by the Chinese mathematician Shih-Chieh Chu in 1303, where it was said to be old knowledge. In about 1150, the Hindu mathematician Bhaskara Acharya gave a very clear explanation of the n-choose-k numbers.

There is a simple combinatorial proof of the relationship $\binom{n}{k} = \binom{n-1}{k-1} + \binom{n-1}{k}$.

Suppose you have n objects and wish to choose k of them. Call one of them x and set it aside. Any combination of k objects out of n either includes x or it doesn't. The number of the ones that include x is $\binom{n-1}{k-1}$ (we need to choose the remaining $k-1$ out of $n-1$). The number of the ones that do not include x is $\binom{n-1}{k}$. The sum of these two terms is the total number of ways to choose k objects from n objects.

Exercises

1.   Write a program that prompts the user for a positive number n and prints out a list of the binomial coefficients $\binom{n}{0}, \binom{n}{1}, ..., \binom{n}{n}$. ⸯ Hint: see Question 4 in Section 8.5. ⸰

2.   If a set A has n elements, the total number of its subsets (including the empty set and the whole set A) is $\binom{n}{0} + \binom{n}{1} + ... + \binom{n}{n}$. Using this fact, derive a formula for this sum. ✓

3.   Derive the formula for $\binom{n}{0} + \binom{n}{1} + ... + \binom{n}{n}$ (see Question 2) in a different way, using the binomial theorem. ⸯ Hint: consider $(1+1)^n$. ⸰

4.   Show that

$$\sum_{k=0}^{n} 2^k \binom{n}{k} = \binom{n}{0} + 2\binom{n}{1} + 4\binom{n}{2} + ... + 2^n\binom{n}{n} = 3^n ✓$$

5.   Show that

$$\sum_{k=0}^{n} \binom{n}{k}(-1)^k = \binom{n}{0} - \binom{n}{1} + \binom{n}{2} - ... + (-1)^n\binom{n}{n} = 0$$

6. Show that

$$\binom{n}{0}^2 + \binom{n}{1}^2 + \dots + \binom{n}{n}^2 = \binom{2n}{n}$$

⸙ Hint: $(x+y)^{2n}$ is the same polynomial as $(x+y)^n(x+y)^n$. Compare the coefficients at $x^n y^n$ when you expand each of these representations. ⸙

7. Write a program that prompts the user for a positive number n and prints the first n rows of Pascal's Triangle. Do not multiply any polynomials in this program — just build the next row of the triangle from the preceding row using the relationship $\binom{n}{k} = \binom{n-1}{k-1} + \binom{n-1}{k}$.

8. Let's slice Pascal's Triangle into diagonal bands as shown below:

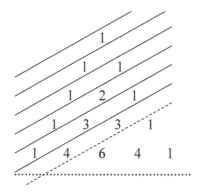

Let's take the sum of the binomial coefficients in each band. Guess what sequence these sums form and show that your guess is correct.

9. Show that for any $n \geq 1$, $\binom{2n}{n} \leq \binom{2n}{n-1} + \binom{2n}{n+1}$ ⸙ Hint: use Pascal's Triangle. ⸙ ✓

10. Show that for any $n \geq 1$, $(2n)! \geq 3^{n-1}(n!)^2$. Hint: use Pascal's Triangle, Question 9, and mathematical induction. ⸙ ✓

12.5   Review

Terms and formulas introduced in this chapter:

> *Polynomial*
> *Coefficient of a polynomial*
> *Degree of a polynomial*
> *Linear polynomial*
> *Quadratic polynomial*
> *Long division (for polynomials)*
> *Remainder theorem*
> *Factor theorem*
> *Binomial coefficient*
> *Binomial theorem*
> *Pascal's Triangle*

$$P(x) = Q(x)(x - c) + P(c)$$

c is a root of $P(x)$ if and only if $(x - c)$ is a factor of $P(x)$.

If $a_n x^n + \ldots + a_1 x + a_0$ has n roots $c_1, c_2, \ldots, c_n$, then
$$a_n x^n + \ldots + a_1 x + a_0 = a_n (x - c_1)(x - c_2)\ldots(x - c_n).$$

$$(x + y)^2 = x^2 + 2xy + y^2$$
$$(x - y)^2 = x^2 - 2xy + y^2$$

$$(x + y)^3 = x^3 + 3x^2 y + 3xy^2 + y^3$$
$$(x - y)^3 = x^3 - 3x^2 y + 3xy^2 - y^3$$

$$(x + y)^n = \binom{n}{0} x^n + \binom{n}{1} x^{n-1} y + \ldots + \binom{n}{n} y^n = \sum_{k=0}^{n} \binom{n}{k} x^{n-k} y^k$$

13 Probabilities

13.1 Prologue

When we roll a pair of dice, what is the likelihood of getting a sum of 11 points? Which is more likely, 7 or 11? If we roll two dice 100 times, approximately how many times will we get 11? Probability theory helps answer such questions.

The probability of an event is a number between 0 and 1 that describes the likelihood of that event happening when we repeat an experiment many times. Zero means the event never happens; 1 means the event always happens, and 0.5 means the event happens roughly half of the time.

To ask and answer questions about probabilities, we first need to describe formally what an event is, and figure out a way to calculate the probability of an event.

Suppose we have an experiment that produces some outcome (a number, an object, or a particular combination of objects). The set of all possible outcomes is called the *probability space* for the experiment. In this book, we will deal only with experiments that have a finite number of possible outcomes. In other words, the probability space is a finite set. For example, when we roll a die with 1, 2, 3, 4, 5, and 6 on its faces, there are six possible outcomes, so the probability space is a set of six elements, {1, 2, 3, 4, 5, 6}.

An *event* is defined as a subset of the probability space that consists of all "favorable" outcomes that meet certain criteria. For example, we can define the following event: the number of points on the die is 3 or more. This event can be described as the set {3, 4, 5, 6}. Other examples of events: the number of points on the die is an even number: {2, 4, 6}; the number of points is 6: {6}. In the latter case, the event is a subset of the probability space that has only one element.

13.2 Calculating Probabilities by Counting

> When all outcomes in the probability space are <u>equally likely</u>, the probability of an event is defined as the ratio of the number of favorable outcomes to the number of all possible outcomes:
>
> $$\text{The probability of an event} = \frac{\text{The number of favorable outcomes}}{\text{The number of all possible outcomes}}$$

Example 1

When we roll a six-sided die with 1, 2, 3, 4, 5, and 6 on its faces, what is the probability of getting 3 or more?

Solution

There are 6 possible outcomes. All six are equally likely (assuming, of course, that the die is a perfect cube and not "loaded"). Four of the outcomes give 3 points or more: {3, 4, 5, 6}. Therefore, the probability of getting 3 or more is $\frac{4}{6} = \frac{2}{3}$.

❖   ❖   ❖

The situation is a little more complicated when we roll a pair of dice. How do we define the probability space here? Let us say that any combination of points on the first die and on the second die is a different outcome. Then the probability space will consist of 36 elements (Figure 13-1). Again, each of the 36 different outcomes is equally likely.

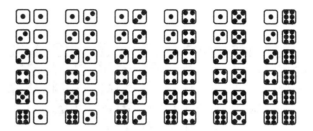

Figure 13-1. The probability space for possible rolls of two dice has 36 elements — all possible combinations of points on the first and the second die.

Example 2

When we roll a pair of dice, what is the probability that the sum of the points on the dice is 11? What is the probability of getting 7?

Solution

The probability of getting 11 can be calculated as 2/36 = 1/18, because exactly two possible outcomes produce a sum of 11 points: 5-6 and 6-5. The probability of getting a 7 is 6/36 = 1/6 because six possible outcomes give a sum of 7 points: 1-6, 2-5, 3-4, 4-3, 5-2, and 6-1 (Figure 13-2).

> When the whole probability space is split into several non-overlapping events, the sum of the probabilities of these events is always 1.

Figure 13-2 shows an example.

Sum =

| 2 | 3 | 4 | 5 | 6 | 7 | 8 | 9 | 10 | 11 | 12 |

$$\frac{1}{36} + \frac{2}{36} + \frac{3}{36} + \frac{4}{36} + \frac{5}{36} + \frac{6}{36} + \frac{5}{36} + \frac{4}{36} + \frac{3}{36} + \frac{2}{36} + \frac{1}{36} =$$

$$= \frac{36}{36} = 1$$

**Figure 13-2. Probabilities of getting a certain sum of points
on a pair of dice.**

You might be wondering: if we are interested in the sum of points on two dice, why not choose a simpler probability space that contains only 11 elements: the possible sums 2, 3, ..., 12? Technically we could, but such a probability space wouldn't be very useful because, as we have seen, different outcomes in this space have <u>different</u> probabilities. This probability space wouldn't help us calculate the probability of each outcome, nor the probabilities of various other events.

> **When we construct a probability space for a problem, we always try to choose a space in which all outcomes have <u>the same probability</u>.**

In such a space, the probability of each outcome is $1/n$, where n is the number of all possible outcomes. We then can find the probability of an event simply by counting the number of outcomes that meet the criteria for the event and dividing that count by n.

Sometimes we can define the probability space in different ways for the same situation, but we should always get the same result for the probability of the same event.

Example 3

If we pull two random cards from a deck of 52 cards, what is the probability of getting two aces?

Solution

We can define the probability space as the set of all pairs of cards (disregarding the order of the two cards in the pair). There are $\binom{52}{2} = \dfrac{52 \cdot 51}{2}$ ways to choose a pair of cards from a deck of 52 cards. There are $\binom{4}{2} = \dfrac{4 \cdot 3}{2}$ ways to choose a pair of aces out of 4 aces (favorable outcomes). The answer is $\dfrac{4 \cdot 3}{2} \Big/ \dfrac{52 \cdot 51}{2} = \dfrac{4 \cdot 3}{52 \cdot 51} = \dfrac{1}{221}$.

Alternative solution: we can define the probability space as the set of all <u>ordered</u> pairs of cards. The number of elements in this space is $52 \cdot 51$. The number of ordered pairs of aces is $4 \cdot 3$. We get the same answer: $\dfrac{4 \cdot 3}{52 \cdot 51} = \dfrac{1}{221}$.

Example 4

If we toss a coin three times, what is the probability of getting heads exactly twice?

Solution

The probability space here is {HHH, HHT, HTH, HTT, THH, THT, TTH, TTT}, and the desirable outcomes are {HHT, HTH, THH}. The answer is 3/8.

Exercises

1. If you make a random guess, what is the probability of your guessing the right answer to a multiple-choice question with 5 answer options? ✓

2. If you roll two dice, what is the probability that the sum of the points is greater than 7?

3. What is the probability of winning the grand prize in a lottery where you have to mark the correct six squares on a grid of 36 squares? ✓

4. If you toss a coin 5 times, what is the probability of getting tails at least 4 times?

5. A roulette has 36 slots numbered 1 through 36 plus 2 slots, marked zero, that win for the "house." The 36 slots alternate 18 red and 18 black; the zeros are green. What is the probability of winning if you bet on 17? What is the probability of winning if you bet "on red" (you win if the ball hits any red slot)?

6. What is the probability that a randomly selected number chosen from the first 50 positive integers is divisible by 3? ✓

7. What is the probability that the two digits in a randomly selected two-digit positive integer (that is, an integer between 10 and 99) are the same?

8.▪ Write a Python program that calculates the probabilities of getting different sums of points (from 3 to 18) when you roll three dice. What sum has the highest probability? ⸾ Hint: initialize a list of counts, all set to 0, then generate all possible combinations of points on three dice and for each combination increment the appropriate count. ⸾

13.3 More Probabilities by Counting

As we know, to calculate the probability of an event we have to count the number of all "favorable" outcomes and divide it by the number of all possible outcomes. When we do the counting, we can rely on all the tricks of the trade that we learned when practicing with combinatorics problems in Chapter 8.

Example 1

If a random poker hand of five cards is dealt from a deck of 52 cards, what is the probability of getting "two pairs" (that is, a pair of the same rank, a pair of another rank, and any fifth card of a third rank)?

Solution

The total number of ways to deal a five-card hand is $\binom{52}{5} = \dfrac{52 \cdot 51 \cdot 50 \cdot 49 \cdot 48}{5 \cdot 4 \cdot 3 \cdot 2 \cdot 1} = 52 \cdot 51 \cdot 10 \cdot 49 \cdot 2$. To form "two pairs," let's first choose the 2 ranks of the pairs out of 13. There are $\dfrac{13 \cdot 12}{2} = 78$ ways to do that. Within each rank, there are 6 ways to choose 2 cards out of 4. Finally there are 44 ways to choose the remaining card (out of the remaining 11 ranks). The answer is $\dfrac{78 \cdot 6 \cdot 6 \cdot 44}{52 \cdot 51 \cdot 10 \cdot 49 \cdot 2} = \dfrac{198}{4165} \approx 0.048$.

Example 2

There are 60 jelly beans in a bag: 15 red, 15 blue, 15 green, and 15 yellow. Danny has pulled out one red and one blue, and 58 jelly beans remain in the bag. If Danny pulls out three more jelly beans at random, what is the probability that he will end up with exactly three jelly beans of the same color?

Solution:

We will use the addition and multiplication rules of counting. There are four mutually exclusive possibilities for a desirable outcome: Danny can end up with three red, three blue, three green, or three yellow jelly beans. To get three red he needs to choose 2 of the 14 red jelly beans remaining in the bag. There are $\binom{14}{2} = \dfrac{14 \cdot 13}{2} = 91$

ways of doing that. Then he needs to choose one more jelly bean, not red. There are $58 - 14 = 44$ ways of doing that. Therefore, there are $91 \cdot 44 = 4004$ ways of getting five jelly beans with three reds among them. The same for three blue jelly beans. To get three green jelly beans, Danny needs to choose 3 out of 15. There are $\binom{15}{3} = \dfrac{15 \cdot 14 \cdot 13}{3 \cdot 2} = 455$ ways of doing that. Similarly, there are 455 ways to choose

three yellow jelly beans. The total number of desirable outcomes is $4004 + 4004 + 455 + 455 = 8918$. The total number of all possible outcomes is the number of ways to choose 3 jelly beans out of 58, which is $\binom{58}{3} = \dfrac{58 \cdot 57 \cdot 56}{3 \cdot 2 \cdot 1} = 30856$. The probability of getting exactly three of the same

color is $\dfrac{8918}{30856} \approx 0.289$.

> When we calculate the probability as a ratio of the number of desirable outcomes to the number of all possible outcomes, it is very important that all possible outcomes in the probability space have equal probabilities. If that is not the case, then the simple ratio method will result in a wrong answer.

Example 3

Consider a game between two players. Each tosses a coin up to three times. Whoever gets heads first wins; if both get the same side they play a tiebreaker; if they get the same side again, they play another tiebreaker. What is the probability that the first player will win?

Solution

In a naive approach we would consider all possible runs of the game:

Player A wins:

A : H   HH   TH   HHH   HTH   THH   TTH

B : T   HT   TT   HHT   HTT   THT   TTT

$$7$$

Player B wins:

A : T   HT   TT   HHT   HTT   THT   TTT

B : H   HH   TH   HHH   HTH   THH   TTH

$$7$$

Tie:

A : HHH   HHT   HTH   HTT   THH   THT   TTH   TTT

B : HHH   HHT   HTH   HTT   THH   THT   TTH   TTT

$$8$$

It seems that the probability of Player A winning is $\dfrac{7}{7+7+8} = \dfrac{7}{22}$. Wrong answer!

The 22 possible runs of the game, listed above, are <u>not</u> equally likely. To see this, let us allow each player to toss three times, no matter what, and only then determine the winner:

Player A wins:

A : H   HH   TH   HHH   HTH   THH   TTH

B : T   HT   TT   HHT   HTT   THT   TTT

↓   ↓   ↓   ↓   ↓   ↓   ↓

A : H**   HH*   TH*   HHH   HTH   THH   TTH

B : T**   HT*   TT*   HHT   HTT   THT   TTT

16   4   4

$$28$$

Here $\star$ is a wildcard character that can stand for either side of the coin. This new probability space is properly defined, with all outcomes equally likely. The old space did not have this property: as we can see now, the H/T game was actually four times more likely than the HH/HT game and 16 times more likely than the HHH/HHT game.

The total number of possible outcomes in the new space is $2^6 = 64$; the correct answer is $\dfrac{28}{64} = \dfrac{7}{16}$.

In this example we do not have to count all the winning combinations: there is a shortcut based on the symmetry of the players. The total number of outcomes is 2^6; the number of tie-game outcomes is 2^3; so the number of outcomes where Player A wins is $\dfrac{\left(2^6 - 2^3\right)}{2} = 28$.

Exercises

1. What is the probability of getting a "four of a kind" poker hand (four cards of the same rank plus any fifth card)? ✓

2.■ A "royal flush," is the best possible poker hand: ace, king, queen, jack, and ten in the same suit. What is the probability of getting a royal flush when you are randomly dealt five cards from a standard deck of 52 cards? ✓

3.■ In the game of "ten-spot" Keno you mark 10 "spots" (numbers) on a playing card that has 80 numbers. The "house" (that is, the casino) then picks 20 numbers randomly. To win the "grand prize" you need to have all 10 of your numbers "hit" by the house numbers. What is the probability of winning the grand prize? (The game of Keno was brought to the United States from China and quickly became popular in casinos, gambling establishments, and even state lotteries. This game gives the player the <u>worst</u> odds of winning of any casino game.) ✓

4.♦ A bag has 3 red marbles and 5 blue marbles. If you randomly pull out 4 marbles, what is the probability of getting two red ones and two blue ones?

5.◆ You draw cards from a deck of 52 cards until you get two cards of the same rank. What is the probability that you'll end up with no more than three cards? ✓

6.◆ The pages in a book are numbered from 1 to 96. We cut out all the page numbers and cut them into individual digits. What is the probability that the sum of two digits chosen at random from this pile will be 10?

7.◆ Sixteen billiard balls are randomly dropped into 6 pockets. What is the probability that the northeast corner pocket has fewer than three balls? ✓

8.◆ What is the probability that a random Blackjack hand of 3 cards has 21 points? In Blackjack, each number card counts at face value, 2 through 10; any ace counts as 1 or 11, your choice; any other "picture" card (jack, queen, or king) counts as 10. ✓

13.4 Multiplication, Addition, and Subtraction

Remember how we used multiplication, addition, and subtraction for counting? We can, of course, apply these methods when we count "favorable" outcomes and all possible outcomes of an experiment. But there is a shortcut: we can apply multiplication, addition, and subtraction directly to probabilities. Let's start with multiplication.

> **Suppose we have two experiments that are independent of each other. Suppose event *A* can occur in the first experiment and event *B* can occur in the second experiment. The probability that both *A* and *B* happen in their respective experiments is the probability of *A* times the probability of *B*.**

Example 1

What is the probability of getting two sixes when we roll a die twice in a row?

Solution

The probability of getting a six on the first roll is $\frac{1}{6}$ and the probability of getting a six on the second roll is $\frac{1}{6}$. The probability of getting two sixes in a row is $\frac{1}{6} \cdot \frac{1}{6} = \frac{1}{36}$. Note that rolling a die twice is the same as rolling two identical dice together.

Example 2

I have three envelopes. Two of them hold one dollar bill; the third is empty. You are allowed to take any two envelopes. What is the probability that you will end up with two dollars?

Solution

When you take the first envelope, the probability of getting a dollar is $\frac{2}{3}$. If you got the first dollar, the probability of getting the second dollar from the remaining two envelopes is $\frac{1}{2}$. The probability of getting two dollars is $\frac{2}{3} \cdot \frac{1}{2} = \frac{1}{3}$. Here we assume that the first experiment was successful before we proceed with the second, but the multiplication rule still works. This is analogous to counting combinations with no repetitions, as we discussed in Section 8.3.

> **Probabilities can be multiplied in two circumstances: (1) When the events are independent from each other, as in Example 1 above or (2) when the probability of the second event is calculated based on the assumption that the first event has already occurred, as in Example 2 above.**

Example 3

On the Caribbean island of Nevis it rains, on average, 45 days in a year. What is the probability of rain on two consecutive days?

Solution

This is a trick question. You might be tempted to apply the multiplication rule and say that the probability is $\frac{45}{365} \cdot \frac{45}{365}$ or $\frac{45}{365} \cdot \frac{44}{364}$. However, the multiplication rule requires that the events happen <u>independently from each other</u>. Not so with weather: September and October are the rainy months on Nevis, and in those months rain on two consecutive days is quite likely. Suppose, for the sake of argument, that on some Mystery Island the 45 rainy days are always September 1 through October 15, and it never rains at all the rest of the year. Then, if we choose two consecutive days in a year randomly, the probability of having rain on both will be $\frac{44}{365}$. We cannot answer the original question about Nevis without additional information about the distribution of rainy days throughout the year.

❖   ❖   ❖

We use addition when we need to find the probability of an event that can be split into two non-overlapping events.

Example 4

In the casino game of Craps, you roll two dice. If you roll 7 or 11, you win. If you roll 2, 3, or 12, you lose. Otherwise the game continues. What are the probabilities of winning and losing on the first roll?

Solution

The probability of winning on the first roll is $\frac{6}{36} + \frac{2}{36} = \frac{2}{9}$ (see Figure 13-2); the probability of losing on the first roll is $\frac{1}{36} + \frac{2}{36} + \frac{1}{36} = \frac{1}{9}$. (This is not the end of the game, though. The rules are such that ultimately the casino wins more than half of the games.)

Example 5

In a *random walk*, you choose the direction of each next step — forward, back, left, or right — randomly, with equal probabilities. What is the probability of returning to the starting position after two steps?

Solution

The following four sequences return to the starting position after two steps: {forward, back}, {back, forward}, {left, right}, and {right, left}. The probability of each sequence is $\dfrac{1}{4} \cdot \dfrac{1}{4} = \dfrac{1}{16}$. The probability that any one of the four sequences takes place is $\dfrac{1}{16} + \dfrac{1}{16} + \dfrac{1}{16} + \dfrac{1}{16} = \dfrac{1}{4}$.

> **If the probability of an event happening is p, the probability of the same event not happening is $1 - p$.**

Example 6

The probability of Dave hitting a home run is 0.13. What is the probability that Dave won't hit a home run?

Solution

$1 - 0.13 = 0.87$.

Example 7

Emily hits the "bull's eye" with a dart on average one out of fifteen times. What is the probability that Emily will hit the bull's eye at least once in three attempts?

Solution

Suppose the probability that Emily hits the bull's eye is p. Then the probability that she misses is $1-p$. The probability that she will miss three times in a row is $(1-p)^3$. The probability that she will hit the bull's eye at least once out of three attempts is $1-(1-p)^3$. Here $p=\dfrac{1}{15}$. The answer is $1-\left(1-\dfrac{1}{15}\right)^3 = \dfrac{631}{3375} \approx 0.19$.

Exercises

1.   What is the probability of rolling 3 on a die three times in a row? ✓

2.   In Scrabble^{TM} there are 98 tiles with letters written on them. There are 2 Bs, 9 As, and 6 Ts. If you pull three tiles randomly out of the box, each time returning the tile into the box, what is the probability of getting B, A, T, in that order?

3.   What is the probability of rolling a die 3 times and never getting a 6? What is the probability of getting a 6 at least once? ✓

4.■   What is the probability that in a random walk you return to the starting position after four steps?

5.■   In the game of squash, an unbroken sequence of successive strokes is called a rally. To win a point when you are serving, you need to win the rally. If your opponent served, winning a rally just gives you the right to serve next. If Ellie wins, on average, 4 out of 10 rallies when she serves and 3 out of 10 rallies when her opponent serves, what is the probability that Ellie will get a point after two rallies starting with the opponent's serve? ✓

6.♦   Question 5 describes the rules for scoring in squash. Susan beats Jimmy on average in 2 out of 3 rallies, regardless of who served. If Susan starts out serving, what is the probability that she will win the next point within three rallies? Within five rallies? What is the probability that Susan will win the next point eventually? ⸮ Hint: in the latter case we get an infinite series, but we already know how to handle it... ⸮ ✓

7.♦   What is the probability that a player will win the next point in squash (see
       Question 6) if it is her serve and she is playing an equal opponent (that is,
       each player's probability of winning a rally is 0.5, regardless of who serves)?

8.♦   A dartboard has 20 outer sectors, 20 inner sectors, and a center, called the
       "bull's eye." If, on average, out of 30 tries I hit the bull's eye once, an inner
       sector 5 times (equally likely among them), an outer sector 20 times, and
       miss the board completely 4 times, what is the probability that I will hit the
       same sector (or the bull's eye) twice in a row? ✓

9.♦   In the Tri-State Megabucks lottery you choose six numbers out of 42
       numbers on the ticket. If your numbers match the six drawn by the lottery
       computer, you hit the jackpot. The computer also draws a seventh "bonus"
       number. If you didn't hit the jackpot but your six numbers match any six
       numbers out of seven drawn by the computer (including the bonus number),
       you get a consolation prize of $10,000. There are other prizes, but they are
       relatively small. If a ticket costs $1.00, what jackpot size makes it worth
       playing?

10.♦ A pawn starts on a black square at the lower left corner of the chessboard.
       On each move the pawn moves one square up or to the right, with equal
       probabilities. It stops when it reaches the right or the top edge. What is the
       probability that the pawn will finish on a black square? ⸮ Hint: extend the
       board, so that it forms an equilateral right triangle with the right angle at the
       lower left corner, and extend all paths to its hypotenuse, so that all paths
       become equal in length. ⸮

13.5 Pseudorandom Numbers

Computers are supposed to act predictably: start at the same position, perform the
same steps, and you should get the same result. But sometimes we want the
computer to act randomly. This is useful, for example, in games and in computer
simulations of random processes.

A typical programming language has library functions that generate "random"
numbers. The numbers are generated in software using a certain algorithm, so they
are not really random, but they approximate random behavior. Such numbers are
called *pseudorandom numbers*.

The Python library has a module `random`, which has many functions that generate and return random numbers. To obtain a random integer r in the range $a \le r \le b$, import the function `randint` from the module `random` and call `randint(a, b)`. For example:

```
>>> from random import randint
>>> randint(1,3)
2
>>> randint(1,3)
3
>>> randint(1,3)
1
>>> randint(1,3)
2
>>> randint(1,3)
3
```

(Your display may differ, since `randint` returns a pseudorandom number.)

The function `random` from the same module returns a `float` x in the range $0.0 \le x < 1.0$. For example:

```
>>> from random import random
>>> random()
0.21503763019111777
>>> random()
0.80958843480468412
```

Another function, `choice`, returns a randomly chosen character from a string (or element from a tuple, list, or any other "sequence"). For example:

```
>>> from random import choice
>>> choice('ABC')
'B'
>>> choice('ABC')
'A'
>>> choice('ABC')
'A'
```

The function `shuffle` rearranges the elements of a list in random order. For example:

```
>>> from random import shuffle
>>> lst = [1,2,3,4,5]
>>> shuffle(lst)
>>> lst
[5, 2, 3, 1, 4]
```

❖   ❖   ❖

Sometimes a theoretical solution gives us a formula, but the numbers may be too large or unwieldy to compute. Then a computer can help, either with calculations or by modeling the random process and observing the result. Such models are called *Monte Carlo simulations* (named after the town and popular gambling resort in Monaco).

Example 1

In a group of 25 people, which is more likely: that there are two people who share a birthday, or that everyone's birthday is on a different day?

Solution

Let's assume that a birthday can fall on any of the 365 days. (Ignore leap years.) One approach is to program a Monte Carlo simulation. Generate a random set of 25 birthdays and check whether any two fall on the same day. Repeat, say, 10,000 times, and count how many sets have shared birthdays and how many don't. This program is left to you as an exercise (Question 5).

Another approach to solving the Birthdays problem is to calculate the probability theoretically, using the methods that we have learned. The first person can have a birthday on any of the 365 days, the second person, too, and so on. Using the multiplication rule, we find that there are 365^{25} possible arrangements of birthdays. Using the multiplication without repetitions rule, we conclude that there are $365 \cdot 364 \cdot ... \cdot 341$ arrangements when all 25 people have different birthdays. Therefore, the probability that all people have different birthdays is $p = \dfrac{365 \cdot 364 \cdot ... \cdot 341}{365^{25}}$, and the probability that at least two people have the same birthday is $1 - p$.

Now let's answer the same question for *n* people. There is no extra work involved and we will be able to obtain the "crossing point": the number of people when the probability gets greater than 1/2. Try guessing that number now just to check your intuition!

It seems we have to deal with very large numbers for the numerator and the denominator. For example, 365^{25} has 65 digits. (We found that number using Python.) Python supports big integers, where a number can have any length, limited only by the size of the computer memory. When regular four-byte `int` values get out of range, Python automatically switches to using long values. So in Python, we can just calculate the top and the bottom of the fraction, take their ratio and be done. Other languages, however, do not have a built-in capability for handling very large numbers. Luckily, we can handle this problem more economically, without big integers. Note that we can split the ratio into the product of individual fractions: $\frac{365 \cdot 364 \cdot \dots \cdot 341}{365^{25}} = \frac{365}{365} \cdot \frac{364}{365} \cdot \dots \cdot \frac{341}{365}$. It is easy to compute each fraction here as a `float`. In Question 4, we ask you to complete this program.

Exercises

1. Write and test a Python function that generates a hand of five cards chosen randomly from a deck of 52 cards. Each card is described by a pair (tuple) that holds the card's suit ('S', 'H', 'D', or 'C') and rank (1 through 13). ✓

2. Suppose you have a Python function `getRandomLetter` that returns a random letter of the alphabet (with approximately equal probabilities for all 26 letters). What is the probability that `getRandomLetter` will return three vowels (any of the letters 'A', 'E', 'I', 'O', 'U') in a row?

3. Write a Python function `getRandomLetter` as described in Question 2. Run it three times to see if you get three vowels in a row. Repeat 100,000 times, count how many times you got three vowels in a row, and estimate the probability of such an event. Compare your result to the theoretical probability that you obtained in Question 2. ≶ Hint: use the `in` operator to find out whether a given character is in a string; for example:

```
if getRandomLetter() in 'AEIOU':
    ...
```

4.■   Using the theoretical approach described in this section, write a program that prints out the probabilities that at least two people in a group of *n* have the same birthday, for *n* = 1 through 50, without using big integers. This program is just a few lines of code. The output should look like this:

```
1: 0.000
2: 0.003
3: 0.008

. . .

48: 0.961
49: 0.966
50: 0.970
```

Pay attention to "OBOBs" (off-by-one bugs), as we call the bugs that happen when a loop in your program runs one too few or one too many times. Determine from the printout the value of *n* where the probability becomes greater than 0.5.

5.■   Write a program that implements a Monte Carlo simulation for birthdays. Write a function that generates a list of *n* random birthdays (numbers from 1 to 365) and returns true if all the numbers in the list are different. Call this function a sufficient number of times to estimate the probability that at least two people out of *n* have the same birthday. Compare your result with the theoretical result obtained in Question 4. ⋛ Hint: to find out whether a list of numbers has duplicates, allocate 365 counts and increment the appropriate count for each number in the list. ⋚

6. The function below returns a random positive number from the "sequence" s:

```
def positiveChoice(s):
    lst = [x for x in s if x > 0]
    if len(lst) > 0:
        return choice(lst)
```

Each positive number in the list is equally likely to be chosen. Rewrite this function without creating any temporary list or set of positive numbers from s and without counting their number in advance. ≷ Hint: Suppose r holds a positive number randomly chosen from the first k positive numbers from s. Start with k = 0 and r = None. When you get the next positive number x, you can either keep r unchanged or replace r with x. What should be the probability of replacing r with x? You never know: x may be the last positive number in s. You need to give it a fair chance... ≷

Test your version of positiveChoice by running it, say, 10000 times on (-1, 1, 2, 0, 3, -2, 4, 5, -6) and counting how many times each of the numbers 1, 2, 3, 4, 5 is returned. All the counts should be around 2000; it is highly unlikely that a count differs from 2000 by more than 120. ✓

7. Write and test a Python function that takes an integer k ($1 \le k < 16$) and returns the probability $p(k)$ that a random sequence of 0s and 1s of length k does not have two 1s in a row. ≷ Hint: see Question 16 in Section 7.3. ≷

8. Write a Monte Carlo simulation to estimate $p(k)$ from Question 7 and compare the result with the theoretical result obtained there.

9. Determine a recurrence formula for $p(k)$ from Question 7 and rewrite the function that computes $p(k)$ using that formula. ≷ Hint: use iterations, not recursion. ≷

13.6 Review

Terms introduced in this chapter:

> *Probability*
> *Probability space*
> *Independent events*
> *Multiplication rule for*
> *probabilities*
> *Addition and subtraction*
> *rules for probabilities*
> *Monte Carlo simulations*

Some of the Python features introduced in this chapter:

```
from random import randint
randint(m, n)

from random import random
random()

from random import choice
choice(s)

from random import shuffle
shuffle(lst)
```

14 Matrices, Sets, and Dictionaries

14.1 Prologue

A table is a common way of presenting and analyzing data. For example, a teacher's gradebook may have one row for each student and one column for each test (Figure 14-1). This way the teacher can conveniently see the scores for each assignment and follow the progress of each student.

	Test 1	Test 2	Final
Abbot, David	94	87	85
Brower, Janet	85	90	93
Costello, Emily	90	92	90
Cote, Adam	78	72	65

Figure 14-1. A table in a gradebook

A company manager might arrange sales data by year and by quarter to compare the quarterly figures for each year as well as quarterly fluctuations from year to year (Figure 14-2). And so on — tables are ubiquitous.

	2003	2004	2005	2006
1st Qtr	3,512	3,002	3,623	3,216
2nd Qtr	4,720	4,500	4,295	4,080
3rd Qtr	3,827	3,391	3,994	3,511
4th Qtr	5,008	4,856	4,659	4,388
Total	17,067	15,749	16,571	15,195

Figure 14-2. A table of sales data by year and quarter

In mathematics, a rectangular table of numbers is called a *matrix*. Matrices are important in many branches of mathematics, especially in *linear algebra*, which deals with linear transformations of vectors and solving systems of linear equations.

In this chapter we will learn how to represent tables and matrices in Python programs.

As we saw in Chapter 1, a *set* represents a collection of elements with no duplicate values. Python's built-in function `set` converts a given "sequence" (list, string, tuple, etc.) into a set. A set in Python is implemented as a special data structure (called a *hash table*) that makes searching for a particular element very efficient.

A *dictionary* is another Python structure. A dictionary defines a mapping from a set of *keys* to a set of *values*. All the keys in a dictionary are different from each other. A dictionary associates one value with each key. A dictionary is, therefore, another way to define a function whose domain is a finite set. In this chapter, you will learn how to work with Python sets and dictionaries.

14.2 Tables and Matrices

There is no special structure in Python for representing a two-dimensional table. Typically each row of a table is represented as a list, and the whole table is represented as a list of lists, its rows. For example,

```
1  2  3
4  5  6
```

can be defined as:

```
>>> m = [[1, 2, 3], [4, 5, 6]]
```

Actually, Python lets you split lists between lines, so you can write

```
>>> m =[[1, 2, 3],
        [4, 5, 6]]
```

`m[0]` is the first row of the table, `m[1]` is the second row, and so on. `m[r]` refers to the row with the index `r` (the (r+1)-th row of the table — recall that in Python indices start from 0). The elements in the row with the index `r` are `m[r][0]`, `m[r][1]`, `m[r][2]`, and so on. In the above example, the value of the element `m[0][2]` is 3.

> If m is a table defined as a list of its rows, m[r][c] refers to the element in the row with the index r and the column with the index c. len(m) gives the number of rows; len(m[r]) gives the number of elements in the *r*-th row.

For a rectangular table m in which all rows are the same length, use len(m[0]) for the number of columns.

❖   ❖   ❖

The mathematical term *matrix* usually refers to a rectangular table that contains numbers. Each element of a matrix is numbered by two subscripts: the row number and the column number. For example:

$$A = \begin{pmatrix} a_{11} & a_{12} & a_{13} \\ a_{21} & a_{22} & a_{23} \end{pmatrix}$$

The numbers in the matrix are called *elements* or *entries*. In math, the subscripts usually start from 1; you have to translate them into Python indices (which start from 0) when you represent a matrix in a program.

Example 1

Write a Python function that returns the sum of all the elements of a given matrix.

Solution

```
def sumElements(m):
    sumMrc = 0
    r = 0
    while r < len(m):
        c = 0
        while c < len(m[r]):
            sumMrc += m[r][c]
            c += 1
        r += 1
    return sumMrc
```

Or:

```
def sumElements(m):
    sumMrc = 0
    for row in m:
        for x in row:
            sumMrc += x
    return sumMrc
```

Or, even shorter:

```
def sumElements(m):
    sumMrc = 0
    for row in m:
        sumMrc += sum(row)
    return sumMrc
```

Or, using a list comprehension:

```
def sumElements(m):
    return sum([sum(row) for row in m])
```

In math, a list of n numbers is called an *n-dimensional vector*. For example, a three-dimensional vector (x, y, z) can represent the x, y, z coordinates of a point in space. Let $\vec{x} = (x_1, x_2, ..., x_n)$ and $\vec{y} = (y_1, y_2, ..., y_n)$ be two n-dimensional vectors. Their sum $\vec{x} + \vec{y}$, is defined as a new vector $(x_1 + y_1, x_2 + y_2, ..., x_n + y_n)$.

Example 2

Write a Python function that returns the sum of two given vectors (represented as lists of the same length).

Solution

```
def sumVectors(x, y):
    v = len(x)*[0]   # create a list of the same length as x,
                     #    filled with 0s
    i = 0
    while i < len(x):
        v[i] = x[i] + y[i]
        i += 1
    return v
```

Note that we have to create a vector of the required length before we can store the resulting values in it.

❖ ❖ ❖

A table in Python can hold any types of objects. For example, you can represent a chess position as an 8 by 8 table in which each element either holds a chess piece or None.

You need to create a table before you can store values in it.

Example 3

Write a Python function that creates and returns a table with a given numbers of rows and columns, filled with None values.

Solution

```
def buildTable(nRows, nCols):
    table = []
    for r in range(nRows):
        table.append(nCols*[None])
    return table
```

We start with an empty list of rows table and append a new row to it nRows times. nCols*[None] creates one row: a list of nCols elements, all set to None.

❖ ❖ ❖

In the above example, you might find it wasteful to repeat `nCols*[None]` several times. You might be tempted to take a shortcut: create a row once, then just append it to the table `nRows` times. Like this:

```
def buildTable(nRows, nCols):
    # buggy code!
    table = []
    row = nCols*[None]
    for r in xrange(nRows):
        table.append(row)
    return table
```

At first, everything seems OK:

```
>>> t = buildTable(2, 3)
>>> t
[[None, None, None], [None, None, None]]
```

But try this:

```
>>> t[0][0] = 'Some'
>>> t
```

What do you get?

```
[['Some', None, None], ['Some', None, None]]
```

This is because the rows in your table actually refer to the same list!

Exercises

1. Let $\vec{x} = (x_1, x_2, ..., x_n)$ and $\vec{y} = (y_1, y_2, ..., y_n)$ be two n-dimensional vectors. Their *dot product*, denoted $\vec{x} \cdot \vec{y}$, is defined as $\vec{x} \cdot \vec{y} = x_1 y_1 + x_2 y_2 + x_3 y_3 + ... + x_n y_n$. Write and test a Python function that returns the dot product of two given vectors (represented as lists of the same length). ✓

2. Write and test a Python function that returns the sum of the elements on the main diagonal (upper left to lower right) of a square matrix (represented as a list of lists). (In linear algebra, this value is called the *trace* of the matrix.)

3.   Write and test a Python function that takes a matrix and prints it neatly, as a rectangular table with aligned right-justified columns. Assume that all the entries in the matrix are positive integers with no more than two digits. ✓

4.■   Write and test a Python program that reads a matrix of integers from a text file. Each line in the file holds integer values for the corresponding row of the matrix (separated by spaces or tabs). ⸙ Hint: For testing, use the function from Question 3 to display the resulting matrix. ⸙

5.■   An n by n matrix defines a *linear transformation* (function) on n-dimensional vectors. If $A = \begin{pmatrix} a_{11} & a_{12} & ... & a_{1n} \\ a_{21} & a_{22} & ... & a_{2n} \\ ... & & & \\ a_{n1} & a_{n2} & ... & a_{nn} \end{pmatrix}$ and $\vec{x} = (x_1, x_2, ..., x_n)$, then $A \cdot \vec{x}$ is a new vector $\vec{y} = (y_1, y_2, ..., y_n)$, such that $y_i = a_{i1}x_1 + a_{i2}x_2 + ... + a_{in}x_n$. In other words, y_i is the dot product of the i-th row of the matrix and $\vec{x}$. Write and test a Python function that takes an n by n matrix A and an n-dimensional vector $\vec{x}$ and returns the vector $A \cdot \vec{x}$. ✓

6.◆   Suppose we have two n by n matrices:

$$A = \begin{pmatrix} a_{11} & a_{12} & ... & a_{1n} \\ a_{21} & a_{22} & ... & a_{2n} \\ ... & & & \\ a_{n1} & a_{n2} & ... & a_{nn} \end{pmatrix} \text{ and } B = \begin{pmatrix} b_{11} & b_{12} & ... & b_{1n} \\ b_{21} & b_{22} & ... & b_{2n} \\ ... & & & \\ b_{n1} & b_{n2} & ... & b_{nn} \end{pmatrix}$$

The matrix C in which $c_{ij} = a_{i1}b_{1j} + a_{i2}b_{2j} + ... + a_{in}b_{nj}$ is called the *product* of A and B and denoted as $A \cdot B$ or simply AB. c_{ij} is the dot product of the i-th row in A and the j-th column in B. Write and test a Python function that takes two square matrices of the same size and returns their product. ⸙ Hint: don't forget to create the resulting matrix before you put values into it. ⸙

7.♦ Write a program that prompts the user to enter an odd positive integer n, between 3 and 19, and prints out a magic square of size n. (A magic square holds consecutive numbers from 1 to n^2, so that the sum of the numbers in each row, in each column, and in each of the two diagonals is the same.)

There is a simple method for generating a magic square when its size is an odd number. We start with 1 in the middle of the top row. We try to place the next consecutive number by shifting from the current position diagonally up and to the right by one. If we get out of bounds above the top row, we "wrap around" and take the corresponding spot in the bottom row. Likewise, if we get out of bounds on the right, we wrap around and take the corresponding spot in the left column. If the spot where we want to place the number is already filled, we instead shift down by one from the current position. For example:

14.3 Sets

In Python, values between braces, separated by commas, define a set. For example:

```
>>> nums = {1, 2, 3}
```

Python's built-in function `set` takes a "sequence" (such as a list, a tuple, a srting, or another set) and builds a set of all the <u>different</u> elements from that sequence. For example:

```
>>> nums = set([1, 2, 3, 2, 1])
>>> nums
{1, 2, 3}
```

**set() creates an empty set. {} is an empty <u>dictionary</u> -- see
Section 14.4.**

You might be wondering: Why do we need sets if we already have lists? There are two reasons. First, the implementation of a set in Python uses a special structure, called a *hash table*, which allows you to find any element quickly and to add and remove elements quickly, regardless of the size of the set. Second, a set cannot have duplicates, so if you want to get rid of duplicate values in a list, you can simply construct a set from that list.

If you are looking for a particular value in a list, you pretty much have to scan through the list to find that value (or to become convinced that the value is not in the list). You can try to keep the list in order (for example, a list of names in alphabetical order), which can make searching faster. But then inserting elements in the middle takes more time. A hash table helps to optimize the time for both searching and adding new elements.

We don't want to go into the details of hashing here. The main idea is to store each element in or near a location that is calculated from the value of that element itself. For example, all valid zip codes that start with 417 can be held in a relatively short list (called a *bucket*) attached to the 417-th element in a list of buckets. To find whether 41705 is a valid zip code, we go straight to the 417-th bucket, then look for 41705 only in that bucket. The number of buckets in this example will be 1000 (from 000 to 999). Some of the buckets in a hash table may be empty, so some space may be wasted, but if we need fast performance, we don't mind wasting a little space.

**The elements in a set are not stored in any particular order, and they do
not have indices.**

We usually just want to know whether a given value is in the set. We can tell that by using the in operator:

```
if x in s:
    ...
```

or

```
if x not in s:
    ...
```

For example:

```
if 'Ben' in names:
    print 'Hello, Ben'
```

Occasionally we might need to use a `for` loop to access all the elements in a set, but the `for` loop will produce the elements in an unpredictable order. For example:

```
>>> names = {'Ana', 'Ben', 'Clair'}
>>> for name in names:
        print(name, end = ' ')

Ben Ana Clair
```

> **The `choice` function cannot be applied directly to a set — you need to convert the set into a list first.**

For example:

```
from random import choice
name = choice(list(names))
```

You can apply the built-in functions `len`, `sum`, `max`, and `min` to sets. `len` returns the number of elements in the set. `sum` returns the sum of all elements (assuming that the + operator can be applied to them). `max` and `min` return the largest and the smallest element, respectively, assuming all the elements are comparable to each other.

Python has intersection, union, and difference operators for sets. The symbols for them are `&`, `|`, and `-`, respectively. For example:

```
>>> s1 = {1, 2, 3, 4}
>>> s2 = {1, 3, 5, 7}
>>> s1 & s2
{1, 3}
>>> s1 | s2
{1, 2, 3, 4, 5, 7}
>>> s1 - s2
{2, 4}
```

(`s1-s2` is a set of all the elements from `s1` that are not in `s2`.)

Python also has the *symmetric difference* operator `^`. `s1^s2` is a set of all the elements that are either in `s1` or in `s2`, but not in both. For example:

```
>>> s1 = {1, 2, 3, 4}
>>> s2 = {1, 3, 5, 7}
>>> s1 ^ s2
{2, 4, 5, 7}
```

Note that the same symbols &, |, and ^ are used for the bitwise and, or, and xor operators on integers (see Chapter 7) as for the intersection, union, and symmetric difference of sets. This is not a coincidence, of course: recall the correspondence between the operators on sets and the logical operators (see Chapter 6).

❖   ❖   ❖

A set in Python also has the methods add, update, discard, remove, and issubset. For example, s.add(x) adds x to the set s. s.discard(x) removes x from s if x is in s (and does nothing if it isn't). The set methods are summarized in Appendix D.

Exercises

1.   Write a one-line function allDifferent(word) that returns True if all the letters in word are different. ⸮ Hint: use a set. ⸮ ✓

2.   Can a Python set hold tuples? Lists? Other sets? Explore and explain the results.

3.   Does the choice function (from the random module) work for sets? Explore and explain the result.

4.   Draw a Venn diagram for the symmetric difference of two sets.

5.   Write an expression equivalent to s1^s2 using the &, |, and - operators for sets. ✓

6.   Pretending that the & operator for sets and the intersection method do not exist, write your own function intersection(s1, s2) that returns the intersection of the sets s1 and s2. ✓

7.   Write a function primes(n) that returns a <u>set</u> of all the prime numbers that do not exceed *n*. For example, primes(10) should return {2, 3, 5, 7}. Your function should build the resulting set gradually. Start with an empty set. For all integers *k* from 2 to *n*, if *k* is not divisible by any of the primes in the set, add *k* to the set.

8. ▪ You can create your own hash table as a list of, say, 16 buckets. Each bucket is a list, too. Start with a hash table in which all the buckets are empty. In Python every "hashable" object (such as a number, a string, etc.) has a method `__hash__()`, which returns an integer. For example:

```
>>> 'Amy'.__hash__()
871006000
```

`x.__hash__() % 16` gives you a number in the range from 0 to 15. You can use that number as the index of the bucket in which `x` belongs. If `x` is not in that bucket yet, you can add it to the bucket. Write a function `myOwnSet(lst)` that takes a list of values `lst`, puts them into your hash table, constructed as described above, and returns that table.

9. ◆ In the `myOwnSet` function described in Question 8, make the number of buckets in the hash table a parameter passed to the function. Create an empty table with 30 buckets, then put into it about 100 words from a typical text file or list of words. Find the most populated bucket and print out the number of words in it. ⟨ Hint: write a *helper* function `add(s, word)` that adds `word` to `myOwnSet` `s`. ⟩

14.4 Dictionaries

A *dictionary* in Python establishes a correspondence between a set of *keys* and a set of *values*. Only one value corresponds to each key. (In some other programming languages, such a structure is called a *map*). In mathematical terms, a dictionary defines a function on a set of keys. In practical terms, a dictionary lets you quickly look up a value (an object, a data record, a text segment) associated with a given key. In a database of taxpayers, for example, the key may be a taxpayer's social security number, and his or her record may be the associated value. In the zip code lookup program, the key may be a zip code, and the name of the city or town for that zip code will be the associated value. The set of keys is implemented as a hash table.

You can create a dictionary with initial entries by listing the *key* : *value* pairs within curly braces. For example:

```
coins = {'Quarter' : 25, 'Dime' : 10,
                 'Nickel' : 5, 'Penny' : 1}
```

Another example:

```
states = {
        'AL' : 'Alabama',
        'AK' : 'Alaska',
     # ...
     # ...
        'WY' : 'Wyoming'
     }
```

Sometimes a short dictionary is used to name the fields of a data record for convenience. For example:

```
book = {'title' : 'Green Eggs and Ham',
        'author' : 'Dr. Seuss',
        'isbn' : '0545002850'}
```

d = {} sets d to an empty dictionary.

Once a dictionary is defined, you can refer to its values using a key as an "index." For example:

```
>>> book['author']
'Dr. Seuss'
>>> book['isbn']
'0545002850'
```

You can modify the value associated with a key and add new key-value pairs using similar syntax:

```
>>> book['isbn'] = '9780583324205'
>>> book['price'] = 7.99
>>> book['price']
7.99
```

Note that in the above examples the keys are <u>literal strings</u>, not names of variables.

If d is a dictionary, len(d) returns the number of key-value pairs in d. d.keys() returns a set (more precisely a dict_keys type object) of all the keys in d. Use k in d to test whether the key k is defined in the dictionary d. The statement del d[k] removes the key k and the associated value from the dictionary d.

The dictionary methods are summarized in Appendix D.

❖   ❖   ❖

We said earlier that a dictionary associates a single value with each key. However, nothing prevents us from making that value a list or a tuple, if necessary. For example:

```
spanishEnglish = {
    'abajo' : ['down', 'below', 'downstairs'],
    'presto' : ['quick', 'prompt', 'ready', 'soon']
  }
...
translations = spanishEnglish['presto']
print(translations)
```

The output will be:

```
[quick, prompt, ready, soon]
```

Exercises

1.   Define a dictionary that holds several name-password pairs (with the name used as the key). Write and test a function that takes such a dictionary and a (name, password) pair (represented as a tuple) and returns True if the name is in the dictionary and the password matches the one in the dictionary.

2.   A tune is described by its title, band, and duration in seconds. Define a dictionary for "Alligator" by The Nationals, 4:05. ✓

3.   Suppose in a dictionary all values associated with keys are different. Write a function reverseDictionary(d) that takes such a dictionary and returns a "reverse" dictionary in which each value becomes a key and its key becomes the associated value. For example, reverseDictionary({1:'A', 2:'B'}) should return {'A':1, 'B':2}.

4.■   Write a program that quizzes a student on the capitals of the 50 U.S. states. Create a text file that lists all the states and their capitals. The program reads the file line by line and puts all the state-capital pairs into a dictionary. The program then extracts a set of all the states from the dictionary, and ten times presents a randomly chosen state to the student (without repetition). The program matches each answer (case blind) against the state capital in the dictionary and keeps track of the number of correct answers. At the end, the program displays the number of correct answers.

5.♦   Define a dictionary that can serve as an index for a book. Each key is a word; the associated value is a list of the page numbers of all the pages on which that word occurs. Write and test a function addEntry(d, word, page) that takes such a dictionary d and adds page to the list of page numbers associated with word. If word is already in the dictionary and page is in its list, then page should not be added. If word is not yet in the dictionary, then addEntry should create a new entry for word with page in its list.

14.5 Review

Terms and notation introduced in this chapter:

Matrix	*Hashing*	$\vec{x} \cdot \vec{y}$
Element or entry in	*Hash table*	
a matrix	*Symmetric difference*	$C = AB$
Vector	*Map*	
Dot product	*Dictionary*	
Product of matrices		

Some of the Python features mentioned in this chapter:

```
m = [[1, 2, 3],
     [4, 5, 6]]
nRows = len(m)
nCols = len(m[0])
x = m[i][j]

table = []
for r in range(nRows):
    table.append(nCols*[None])

s = {'A', 'B', 'C'}
if x in s:
    ...
if x not in s:
    ...
emptySet = set()
s1 & s2
s1 | s2
s1 - s2
s1 ^ s2

d = {'K1':'A', 'K2':'B', 'K3':'C'}
x = d[k]
d[k] = x
del d[k]
if k in d:
    ...
allKeys = d.keys()
```

15   Graphs

15.1   Prologue

In the 1700s, the city of Königsberg, then the capital of East Prussia near the Baltic Sea, had seven bridges connecting the banks of the river Pregel with the banks of its tributary and the Kniephof island in the center. No one remembers for sure how the following puzzle came about: to find a path through the city that crosses each of the seven bridges exactly once (Figure 15-1). Legend has it that many citizens took long walks around the city on Sundays trying to solve the puzzle. (Believe it or not, there were many lovers of puzzles in the 1700s, just as there are today.)

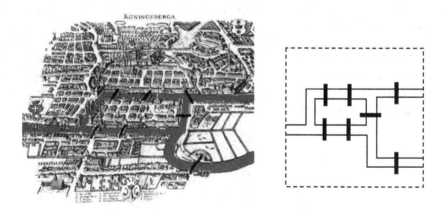

Figure 15-1. The Seven Bridges of Königsberg puzzle

Can you find a solution?

Finally, around 1735, the great Swiss mathematician Leonhard Euler (pronounced "oiler") solved the problem (as he often did when he was interested in one). In the process, Euler founded two new branches of mathematics: topology and graph theory.

To begin with, Euler simplified the picture: he compressed each piece of land into one point and replaced each bridge with a line segment that connected two points, obtaining what is now called a *graph* with four *vertices* and seven *edges* (Figure 15-2).

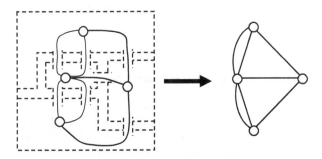

Figure 15-2. The Seven Bridges puzzle represented as a graph

The exact shape of the graph is not important — you can move the vertices around and stretch or bend the edges, as long as the *topology* of the graph (the particular pairs of vertices connected by an edge) remains the same. The task is now to find a continuous path in the graph that traces each edge exactly once. Such a path is called an *Euler path*. Before you tackle the Seven Bridges puzzle, try to find an Euler path in several other graphs (Figure 15-3) and come up with a rule to determine which graphs have an Euler path and which don't (see Question 9 in Section 15.4).

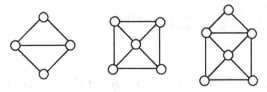

Figure 15-3. Examples of graphs

A graph can be used to represent a computer network, a system of routes for an airline, a road map, a set of possible positions and legal moves in a game, and so on (Figure 15-4). Thus graphs serve as a universal modeling tool. They also have many interesting mathematical properties and are a source of fascinating problems and computer algorithms, some easy and others very difficult.

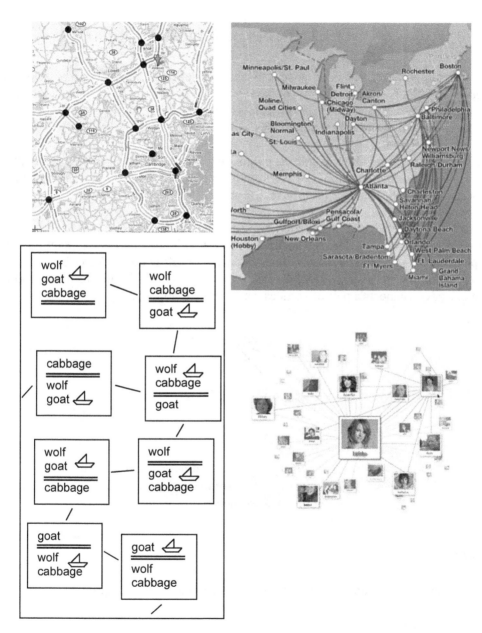

Figure 15-4. Some applications of graphs

15.2   Types of Graphs

A graph can be described in an abstract way, as a set of its *vertices* and a set of its *edges*. An edge is represented by an unordered pair of vertices; it is understood that the edge "connects" that pair of vertices. The vertices of a graph are sometimes called *nodes*, and the edges are sometimes called *arcs*.

Figures 15-2 and 15-3 show graphs as points on a plane connected by line segments. Sometimes mathematicians indeed work with such *planar graphs*. But in general, a drawing of a graph simply helps to visualize it.

A graph can have several edges connecting the same pair of vertices. Such graphs are called *multigraphs*. The Seven Bridges graph (Figure 15-2) is an example. A graph can also have an edge connecting a vertex to itself (Figure 15-5). Such edges are called *loops*. In a *simple graph* (such as those shown in Figure 15-3), no more than one edge connects a pair of vertices, and there are no loops.

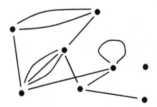

**Figure 15-5.   A *multigraph*: several edges can connect the
same pair of vertices, and some vertices can be
connected to themselves**

Example 1

Describe the simple graph below as a set of vertices and a set of edges.

Solution

First we need to label the vertices of the graph to be able to refer to them. Let's use the numbers from 1 to 4:

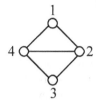

Now $V = \{1,2,3,4\}$, $E = \{(1,2), (2,3), (3,4), (4,1), (2,4)\}$, $G = (V,E)$. Or, in Python:

```
v = {1, 2, 3, 4}
e = {(1, 2), (2, 3), (3, 4), (4, 1), (2, 4)}
g = (v, e)
```

When a graph is used as a model for a real-life situation, its vertices may represent different geographical locations, different objects, or different positions in a game. But if you view a graph as an abstract mathematical object, the graph is defined only by its *topology*; that is, by the configuration of its vertices and edges.

> **A simple graph in which every pair of vertices is connected by an edge is called a *complete graph*.**

A complete graph with n vertices is usually denoted by K_n.

Example 2

Draw K_4 and K_5.

Solution

A complete graph could be drawn differently, but from the point of view of graph theory it would be essentially the same graph as long as it had the same number of vertices and there was one edge connecting every vertex to every other vertex.

Another simple type of graph is one in which the vertices are arranged into a circular sequence and each vertex is connected to two of its neighbors. (Think of a circle of people holding hands.) Such a graph is called a *cycle*. A cycle with n vertices is usually denoted by C_n.

Example 3

Draw C_6.

Solution

Exercises

1.   Find an Euler path in the graph below. ✓

2.   Draw a sketch of the graph $G = (V, E)$, where $V = \{a, b, c, d\}$ and
        $E = \{(a, b), (a, c), (b, c), (b, d)\}$. ✓

3.   Tag the vertices of the graph below with letters or numbers, then describe the
        graph as a set of its vertices and a set of its edges.

4.   Which of the following graphs are simple graphs? Which are multigraphs?
        Which have loops? ✓

(a)   (b)   (c)   (d)

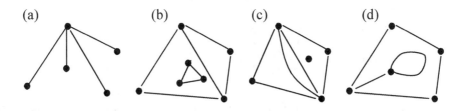

5.   How many edges does C_{12} have?

6.   How many edges does K_{12} have? ✓

7.   For which n is C_n the same as K_n ?

15.3 Isomorphism of Graphs

Two graphs are called *isomorphic* if there exists a one-to-one correspondence between their vertices and a one-to-one correspondence between their edges, such that two vertices are connected by an edge in the first graph if and only if the corresponding vertices are connected by the corresponding edge in the second graph.

Example 1

Consider two graphs: $G_1 = (V_1, E_1)$ and $G_2 = (V_2, E_2)$. The set of the vertices of the first graph is $V_1 = \{A, B, C, D, E\}$; the set of its edges is $E_1 = \{(A,B), (A,C), (B,C), (B,D), (C,E), (D,E)\}$. For the second graph, $V_2 = \{1, 2, 3, 4, 5\}$ and $E_2 = \{(1,2), (2,3), (3,4), (4,5), (5,1), (2,4)\}$. Are G_1 and G_2 isomorphic?

Solution

To find out, let's draw the two graphs:

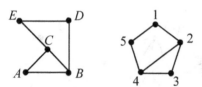

At a first glance, they seem different, but a little bending (without breaking the edges) will convince us that they in fact have the same configuration:

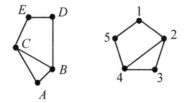

The correspondence $A \leftrightarrow 3$, $B \leftrightarrow 2$, $C \leftrightarrow 4$, $D \leftrightarrow 1$, $E \leftrightarrow 5$ establishes an isomorphism between these two graphs.

Note how we tagged the vertices of a graph to be able to refer to them. We used letters for the first graph and numbers for the second. In general we can use any tags or names.

Isomorphism between graphs has three properties:

1. *Reflexivity*: any graph is isomorphic to itself;
2. *Symmetry*: if G_1 is isomorphic to G_2, then G_2 is isomorphic to G_1;
3. *Transitivity*: if G_1 is isomorphic to G_2 and G_2 is isomorphic to G_3, then G_1 is isomorphic to G_3.

> **A relationship that has these three properties is called an *equivalence relation*.**

An equivalence relation on the elements of a set breaks that set into non-overlapping subsets, called *equivalence classes*. Any two elements in the same equivalence class are "equivalent" to each other (that is, the equivalence relation holds for them), and any two elements in different equivalence classes are not "equivalent."

Since isomorphism is an equivalence relation between graphs, all graphs fall into non-overlapping classes of isomorphic graphs.

Another example of an equivalence relation is the "being connected by a path" relation between two vertices of a graph G. This relation is true for the vertices X and Y if there is a path from X to Y. It is easy to see that the three properties of an equivalence relation are satisfied for this relation. In particular, if X is connected by a path to Y, and Y is connected by a path to Z, then X is connected by a path to Z (just combine the paths — Figure 15-6).

> **A graph is said to be *connected* if any two of its vertices are connected by a path.**

An equivalence class for the "being connected by a path" relation is a set of vertices in a connected subgraph of G. Therefore, any graph is a union of non-intersecting connected subgraphs (Figure 15-6).

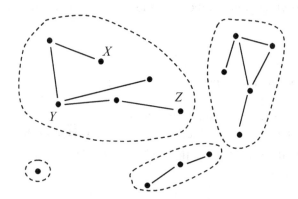

Figure 15-6. A graph can be split in a unique way into non-intersecting connected subgraphs

Exercises

1.   Determine whether the following pairs of graphs are isomorphic: ✓

(a)

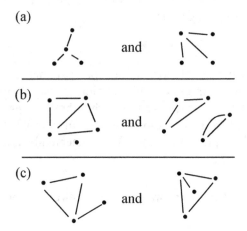

        (b)

        (c)

2.   Is there a different correspondence of vertices for the graphs in Example 1 that demonstrates their isomorphism? If yes, show it; if not, explain why not. ✓

3.   How many different simple graphs with four vertices are there, if you count all isomorphic graphs as one? How many of them are connected? ✓

4.   A graph $G_2 = (V_2, E_2)$ is called a *subgraph* of $G_1 = (V_1, E_1)$ if $V_2 \subseteq V_1$ and $E_2 \subseteq E_1$. Can a graph be isomorphic to its subgraph? Explain. ✓

5.■ Does K_n have a subgraph isomorphic to C_n? Does K_n have a subgraph isomorphic to C_{n-2} when $n \geq 5$? Does K_n have a subgraph isomorphic to K_{n-2} when $n \geq 5$?

6.■ Is $x \leq y$ an equivalence relation on the set of all real numbers?

7.■ Come up with an example of an equivalence relation between two integers, such that each equivalence class has more than one element.

8.■ Come up with an example of an equivalence relation between two sets (other than equality).

15.4 Degree of Vertex

The number of edges that come out of a vertex of a graph is called the *degree* **of that vertex.**

If an edge is a loop (connects a vertex to itself), that edge is counted twice in the degree of that vertex. In a simple graph, the degree of a vertex is simply the number of other vertices to which this vertex is connected.

Example 1

What are the degrees of the vertices in the following multigraph?

Solution

A: 2; B: 4; C: 3; D: 3; E: 4.

If two graphs are isomorphic, the degrees of the corresponding vertices must match, of course.

Exercises

1.   If a graph has n vertices, and $d_1, d_2, ..., d_n$ are their degrees, what is the total number of edges in that graph? ✓

2.   Is it possible to have a graph with five vertices whose degrees are 2, 2, 4, 3, and 6? If yes, give an example; if not, explain why not. ✓

3.   Can a graph have five vertices, each connected to exactly three others? Draw an example or explain why not.

4.   Is it possible to have a group of five colleagues, each corresponding via e-mail with exactly three others?

5.   Prove that the only simple graph with n vertices and the degrees of all the vertices equal to $n-1$ is K_n. ✓

6.■   Prove that the only simple connected graph with three or more vertices and the degrees of all the vertices equal to 2 is C_n. ✓

7.■ Give an example of two graphs with the same number of vertices, such that the degrees of the vertices in the first graph match some permutation of the degrees of the vertices in the second graph, but the graphs are not isomorphic to each other.

8.◆ Show that in any group of six people there are either three who all know each other or three who are all strangers to each other.

‹ Hint:

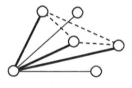

‹

9.◆ Recall that an Euler path traverses all the edges of a graph and passes through each edge exactly once. Show that if a graph has an odd-degree vertex, then an Euler path, if it exists, must begin or end at that vertex.

10. Remove one bridge in the Seven Bridges of Königsberg puzzle so that it becomes solvable. ✓

11. We want to make a wire framework for a cube. We want to bend a single piece of wire so that it covers as many edges of the cube as possible, without doubling over any edge. What is the smallest number of edges that will remain missing?

12.◆ In a graph, suppose L is the number of vertices whose degrees are odd. Describe, in terms of L, a necessary and sufficient condition for the graph to have an Euler path.

13.■ An *Euler circuit* in a graph begins and ends at the same vertex and traverses every edge of the graph exactly once. Describe the necessary and sufficient condition for a graph to have an Euler circuit.

14. Show that for any $n \geq 3$ there is a connected graph with n vertices that has an Euler circuit (as defined in Question 13). ✓

15. For which $n \geq 3$ does K_n have an Euler circuit?

16. Give an example of a connected graph that cannot be turned into a graph with an Euler circuit by removing one or several edges. ✓

17. A *Hamilton circuit* in a graph starts and ends at the same vertex, goes along the edges of the graph, and visits each <u>vertex</u> exactly once. Hamilton circuits are named after an Irish mathematician, Sir William Rowan Hamilton (1805-1865). In 1859, Hamilton designed a puzzle and sold it to a toy maker in Dublin. The puzzle was a regular dodecahedron (a solid with twelve pentagon-shaped faces and 20 vertices), made of wood. Each vertex was labeled with the name of a prominent city. A player had to find a path with the beginning and end at the same vertex that went along the edges and visited each "city" exactly once. Solve Hamilton's original puzzle. Hint: you can work with pencil and paper using a planar graph isomorphic to the dodecahedron:

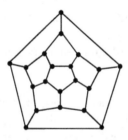

18. Can you find a Hamilton circuit (as defined in Question 17) in the following graph?

15.5 Directed and Weighted Graphs

Graphs described in the previous sections are called *undirected*, because their edges have no direction: a vertex *A* is connected to a vertex *B* if and only if *B* is connected to *A*. We can also consider *directed graphs*, in which edges are arrows that show the direction of the connection (Figure 15-7).

Figure 15-7. A directed graph

In a directed graph, there may be an arrow from vertex *A* to vertex *B* but not from *B* to *A*, or there may be arrows in both directions (Figure 15-8).

**Figure 15-8. A directed graph with a pair of vertices
connected in both directions**

If we have a directed graph, we can associate with it an undirected graph, replacing each arrow with an edge.

Example 1

Draw an undirected graph associated with the directed graph in Figure 15-8.

Solution

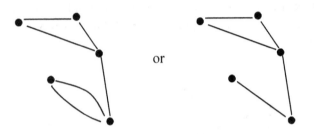

or

depending on how we agree to handle multiple edges between the same two vertices.

❖ ❖ ❖

> **A directed graph is called *connected* if the associated undirected graph is connected.**

Some typical tasks involving directed graphs are to find whether a path exists from one vertex to another along the arrows or to find the shortest such path.

❖ ❖ ❖

A *weighted graph* is a graph with numbers ("weights") associated with its edges. For example, a transit network can be represented by a weighted graph in which the weights are distances between adjacent stations. A computer network can be represented by a weighted graph in which weights represent the costs of transmitting information over the links.

A typical task for a weighted graph is to find an *optimal path* between two given vertices. The sum of the weights along such a path must be the smallest possible.

Example 2

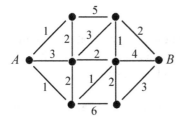

For the weighted graph above, find an optimal path from A to B.

Solution

You can try to list all possible paths, of course, but there are too many of them. A more promising approach is to first find optimal paths to B from each <u>neighbor</u> of A and mark the cost of each such optimal path:

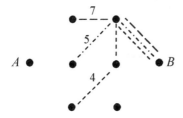

Now we can add the cost of going from A to a neighbor to the cost of going from that neighbor to B and find the best combination:

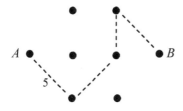

We can do this manually for a small graph, but obviously we'll need a computer program for larger graphs.

Exercises

1.   Define isomorphism for directed graphs. ✓

2.   A cycle in a directed graph is a path along the arrows that starts and ends at the same vertex. Show that if every vertex in a directed graph has at least one arrow coming out of it, then the graph has a cycle.

3.■   Find an optimal path (with the smallest sum of weights along it) from A to B in the following directed graph: ✓

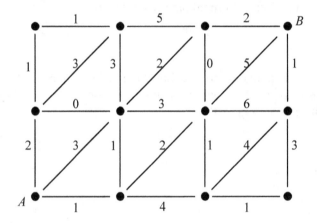

4. In a famous puzzle dating back at least a thousand years, a farmer has a wolf, a goat, and a cabbage. He needs to cross a river and transport his possessions across, too, but his tiny boat can hold only him and one other object or animal. How can he do it without endangering any of his possessions? (The wolf would gobble up the goat in a minute, if left unattended, but she is indifferent to cabbage, while the goat, on the contrary, loves cabbage. The cabbage doesn't like anyone.)

   (a) Represent the puzzle using a directed graph in which each vertex represents a certain position of the farmer and his three possessions on the two banks of the river. What is the total number of all possible positions? Leave only those vertices of the graph in which all the farmer's possessions are safe.

   (b) Draw the arrows in the graph that correspond to the allowed river crossings.

   (c) Find and describe the solution to the puzzle by finding a path from the initial position (all on one bank) to the final position (all on the other bank) along the edges of the graph. How many solutions are there?

5. Four people need to cross a bridge in the dark. They all begin on the same side and they have only one flashlight. A maximum of two people can cross at one time. Any party that crosses, either 1 or 2 people, must have the flashlight with them. The flashlight must be walked back and forth (it may not be thrown, etc.). The four people walk at different speeds: it takes them 1, 2, 5, and 10 minutes, respectively, to cross from one side to the other. What is the optimal strategy and the minimum time required for bringing all four people across the bridge? Can it be accomplished in less than 19 minutes? ⸙ Hint: Represent the problem as a weighted graph where the vertices represent all possible positions and the edges represent allowed crossings; assign a weight — the duration of the crossing — to each edge; find the optimal path from the initial to the final position. ⸙

6. An Euler circuit in a directed graph follows the directions of the edges. Devise a necessary and sufficient condition (in terms of the numbers of arrows coming into and going out of each vertex) for a directed graph to have an Euler circuit.

7.♦   Suppose an undirected graph is represented as a dictionary. Each vertex is a
      key; the value associated with it is the list of all vertices connected to it.
      Write and test a Python function that tries to find an Euler circuit in such a
      graph. The function should return the circuit as a list of vertices in the circuit
      (with the first and the last vertices being the same) or `None` if the graph has
      no Euler circuits.

      ⸘ Hints:

      1. If an Euler circuit exists, you can start at any vertex.

      2. If you have found an Euler circuit in some subgraph, you can try
          expanding it by merging it with another circuit that goes through one of
          the first circuit's vertices.

      ⸘

15.6   Review

Terms and notation introduced in this chapter:

Graph	*Connected graph*	$G = (V, E)$
Vertex or *node*	*Degree of a vertex*	K_n
Edge or *arc*	*Euler path*	C_n
Multigraph	*Euler circuit*	
Loop	*Hamilton circuit*	
Simple graph	*Directed graph*	
Complete graph	*Weighted graph*	
Cycle	*Optimal path*	
Isomorphism,		
isomorphic graphs		
Equivalence relation		
Equivalence classes		

16 More Graphs

16.1 Prologue

In this chapter we continue talking about graphs. Graph theory is a vast and fascinating branch of mathematics; even a very brief and superficial survey did not fit into one chapter. The basic definitions are simple, making it a great playground for amateur mathematicians of all ages. But some of the theorems are very hard.

We will first discuss representation of graphs using adjacency matrices, then talk about coloring geographic maps and planar graphs, which, as we will see, is the same thing, and finally try to tackle the Four Color Theorem for planar graphs.

But first let us recall some of the terms from the previous chapter:

- In a *simple graph*, at most one edge connects any two vertices, and a vertex cannot be connected to itself.

- In a *multigraph*, more than one edge can connect two vertices, and a vertex can be connected to itself.

- In a *directed graph*, edges have directions; they are represented by arrows.

- In a *weighted graph*, a weight (a real number) is assigned to each edge.

- In a *connected graph*, any two vertices are connected by a path.

- C_n is a simple graph with n vertices that consists of one cycle. K_n is a simple graph with n vertices in which every pair of vertices is connected by an edge.

- The degree of a vertex is the number of edges that come out of that vertex.

16.2 Adjacency Matrices

Suppose we have a simple graph with n vertices.

Two vertices connected by an edge are called *adjacent*.

One way to describe the graph's edges is simply to list all pairs of adjacent vertices. But there is another way. We can make a table with n rows and n columns and put a checkmark in the intersection of the *i*-th row and *j*-th column if the *i*-th vertex is connected to the *j*-th vertex. In math and computer programs it is more convenient to use 0s and 1s instead of checkmarks: 1 indicates an edge and 0 no edge. A square matrix that describes the edges of a graph is called the *adjacency matrix* of that graph (Figure 16-1).

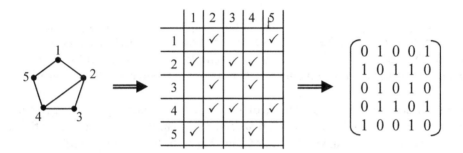

Figure 16-1. Representing a graph by its adjacency matrix

> **For a simple (not directed) graph, its adjacency matrix contains only 0s and 1s, is symmetrical over the main diagonal, and has zeros on the diagonal.**

Example 1

Write the adjacency matrix for the following graph:

Solution

$$\begin{pmatrix} 0 & 1 & 0 & 1 \\ 1 & 0 & 1 & 1 \\ 0 & 1 & 0 & 0 \\ 1 & 1 & 0 & 0 \end{pmatrix}$$

For a directed graph, we can agree that the value a_{ij} in its adjacency matrix is 1 if there is an arrow from the i-th vertex to the j-th vertex. The adjacency matrix for a directed graph is not necessarily symmetrical.

Example 2

Write the adjacency matrix for the following directed graph:

Solution

Assuming the vertices are numbered in order A, B, C, D:

$$\begin{pmatrix} 0 & 0 & 0 & 1 \\ 1 & 0 & 1 & 0 \\ 0 & 0 & 0 & 0 \\ 0 & 1 & 0 & 0 \end{pmatrix}$$

For a multigraph, an element of the adjacency matrix holds the number of edges between the corresponding vertices. For a simple weighted graph, instead of 1s and 0s we can put into the matrix the weights assigned to the edges.

Exercises

1.   Write the adjacency matrix for the following graph: ✓

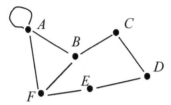

2.   Draw a directed graph that corresponds to the following adjacency matrix:

$$\begin{pmatrix} 0 & 1 & 1 & 0 \\ 0 & 0 & 1 & 0 \\ 1 & 1 & 1 & 0 \\ 0 & 1 & 0 & 0 \end{pmatrix}$$

3.   Write adjacency matrices for C_5 and K_5. ✓

4.▪   Which of the following operations on the adjacency matrix for a directed graph always results in a matrix for an isomorphic graph? (Isomorphism for graphs is defined in Section 15.3.) ✓

   (a)   Flipping the matrix symmetrically over the main diagonal
   (b)   Swapping any two rows
   (c)   Swapping any two columns
   (d)   Swapping the i-th and j-th rows, then the i-th and j-th columns (for any i and j).

5.▪   Write and test a Python function that takes an adjacency matrix for a simple graph and returns a list of its edges. An edge that connects the i-th and j-th vertices should be described by the tuple $(\texttt{i}, \texttt{j})$, where $i < j$.

6.▪   Modify the function from Question 5 so that it works for directed graphs. An arrow from the i-th to the j-th vertex should be described by the tuple $(\texttt{i}, \texttt{j})$.

7.♦   Write and test a Python function that takes a simple graph $G = (V, E)$ (described by two sets, V and E) and returns its adjacency matrix.

8.♦   Suppose A is an adjacency matrix for a directed graph. How can you interpret the values of the elements of $A^2 = A \cdot A$ in terms of existing paths in the graph? ✓

9.♦   Write and test a Python function `allPaths(g, k)` that takes a directed graph `g` (described by two sets, V and E) and a positive integer k and calculates the number p_{ij} of paths of length k from the i-th vertex to the j-th vertex for all i and j. The result should be returned as a matrix with values p_{ij}. ⸮ Hint: see Questions 7 and 8. ⸮

16.3 Coloring Maps

In a geographical map, neighboring regions, countries, or states are often shown in different colors. The map in Figure 16-2 uses five "colors" (five shades of gray, plus white for water).

Figure 16-2. A map colored in five "colors"

Can any map be colored in five colors? Could we use fewer colors? Four colors? Three colors? These questions have little to do with making maps: we could use as many colors as we need to make a pretty map. Instead, these questions end up in the realm of mathematics, as many interesting questions do.

Once we enter the realm of mathematics, though, we must be very precise. What is a map? What is a "country"? What does "neighboring countries" mean? Do "countries" that only touch in one point, like Colorado and Arizona at The Four Corners on a U.S. map, share a border? Can a country be split into two disjoint regions, like Alaska and the mainland United States? Can a country be an island? Several islands? Can a country be entirely inside another country, like San Marino in Italy?

We need formal definitions, and in this case they get rather messy. Let's assume that each "country" is one contiguous region. Pick a "capital city" in each country. For each pair of neighboring countries, build a "road" to connect their capital cities in such a way that the road crosses a segment of the shared border and stays entirely within the area of the two countries. Do not allow two roads to cross each other. What you get is a *planar graph* — a graph drawn on the plane (Figure 16-3). The edges do not have to be straight line segments, but they cannot intersect.

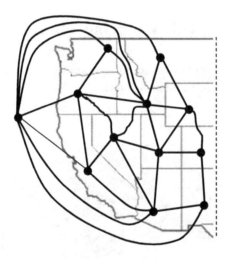

Figure 16-3. A planar graph corresponds to a geographical map

The problem of coloring a map becomes the problem of coloring the vertices of the corresponding planar graph. (It is not practical, of course, to "color" points; we simply assign them colors or numbers or symbols.)

> **A graph is called *properly colored* if any two adjacent vertices are colored in different colors.**

In coloring problems we consider only connected graphs, because if a graph is not connected, we can color each connectivity component separately.

Figure 16-4 shows the graph from Figure 16-3 properly colored in four colors, represented by the numbers 1 through 4.

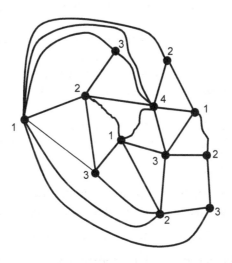

Figure 16-4. A planar graph properly colored in four colors

Exercises

1.   Properly color the graph below in two colors. ✓

2.   Remove one vertex of degree 2 from the periphery of the graph in Question 1, merging the two edges that come out of it into one. Can the resulting graph be properly colored in two colors?

3.   Suppose a graph is properly colored in two colors. What can you tell about the colors of the two vertices that are the endpoints of a path of a certain length? When are they the same? When different?

4.   Suppose a graph is properly colored in two colors, and A and B are two vertices connected by an edge. Consider any two paths from A and B, respectively, to a third vertex C. What can you tell about the parities of the lengths of these paths? Are they even or odd?

5.■   Formulate the necessary and sufficient condition for a graph to be properly colorable in two colors. State your condition in terms of the absence of certain type of subgraphs in a graph. Justify your answer, by showing that this is indeed a necessary and sufficient condition. ✓

6.◆   Write and test a Python function that colors a given graph in two colors or establishes that it can't be done. Use the following "brute-force" algorithm:

1.   Color any one vertex.

2.   For each vertex that is already colored, find its neighbors that are not yet colored. Assign to each neighbor the appropriate color.

3.   Repeat Step 2 until all the vertices are colored.

4.   Check whether the graph is properly colored; return None if it isn't.

Assume that the input graph is represented by an n-by-n adjacency matrix, and return the result as a list of 1s and 2s that holds the colors of the vertices corresponding to the rows of the matrix.

7.   Consider the following graph:

Convince yourself that in any proper coloring of this graph in three colors, the colors of the vertices A and B are the same. Now, for any $N \geq 2$, give an example of a "longer" graph with similar properties:

a)   it is colorable in three colors;

b)   it has two vertices A and B such that the distance between them (the length of the shortest path) is greater than or equal to N;

c)   in any proper coloring of the graph in three colors, the colors of A and B are the same.

8. None of the following graphs is colorable in three colors:

Clearly, if you take any odd cycle, and connect all its vertices to one "central" vertex, the resulting graph cannot be colored in three colors. Any graph that contains one of these "odd cartwheels" as a subgraph cannot be colored in three colors either. Come up with an example of a graph that does not contain an "odd cartwheel" and still is not colorable in three colors.
⚅ Hint: see Question 7. ⚅

9. Give an example of a graph in three-dimensional space that cannot be colored in three colors and contains no "triangles" (that is cycles of length 3). ⚅ Hint: you will need at least eleven vertices. ⚅ ✓

16.4 The Four Color Theorem

The Four Color Conjecture states that any planar graph can be colored in four colors. It first came up in the middle of the 19th century, but the proof had evaded mathematicians for a long time. Many amateurs and professionals tried to show the conjecture to be false by coming up with a counterexample: a map or a graph that cannot be colored in four colors. They failed. Finally, the Four Color Theorem was proved in the late 1970s by Kenneth Appel and Wolfgang Haken. Their proof, published in 1977, was unorthodox: they had to analyze many graph configurations, for which they used a computer program. It required 1200 hours of computer time to complete the proof. (These days it would take less time, of course.) Many mathematicians remained skeptical, though, because they could not verify the proof independently. In 1996 Neil Robertson, Daniel P. Sanders, Paul Seymour and Robin Thomas published a shorter and a more manageable proof,[*] still based on Appel's and Haken's ideas.

In this section we will make a naïve attempt to prove the theorem. We will largely follow the ideas of the British mathematician Alfred Kempe, who proposed his proof at the end of the 1870s. Kempe's proof stood unchallenged for about 10 years, until a major flaw was found in it. We'll go as far as we can with our proof, and see what we can learn from it. At the end you yourself will discover and explain the flaw (see Question 10 in the exercises).

_____

[*] http://people.math.gatech.edu/~thomas/FC/fourcolor.html

As often happens in proofs of theorems about graphs, we try to use mathematical induction. The idea is to somehow reduce a graph with n vertices to a smaller graph by eliminating one or several vertices. The smaller graph has the desired property by the induction hypothesis. We then try to restore the eliminated vertices in such a way that the property still applies. One has to be very careful doing all this (see Question 5 in the exercises).

One way to reduce the number of vertices in a graph is to "glue together" two vertices. If A and B are two vertices, we can replace them with one vertex O. We connect O to a vertex X with an edge if A <u>or</u> B (or both) are connected to X. (Question 2 in the exercises offers an example of "gluing together" two vertices.) We can glue together three or more vertices in the same way.

Another idea is to split a graph into smaller graphs, then, knowing that each of them has the desired property, combine them back into the original graph, while maintaining the property (see Question 3 in the exercises).

The edges of a planar graph divide the plane into regions, with one infinite outer region. If a graph is properly colored, and you remove one or several edges, the resulting graph will be properly colored, too. When proving theorems about coloring planar graphs, we can consider only the worst-case scenario, in which no edge can be added to the graph. This happens when all the regions are "triangles" (that is, are bounded by three edges). Such planar graphs are called *fully triangulated*. We can convert any planar graph into a fully triangulated graph by adding a few "diagonals" to every region (see an example in Question 4 in the exercises). If we can color this fully triangulated graph in p colors, then we can color the original graph in p colors, too.

We are now done with the preliminaries and can proceed with our "proof." We will use mathematical induction by the number of vertices in the graph. Clearly any graph with 4 or fewer vertices can be colored in four colors (the base case). Let us take a graph with n vertices, $n > 4$. We assume (induction hypothesis) that any planar graph with fewer than n vertices can be colored in four colors and try to prove that our graph with n vertices can be colored in four colors, too.

Without loss of generality, we can assume that our graph is fully triangulated. Moreover, if any of the triangles has vertices both inside and outside, the problem of reducing the graph into smaller subgraphs is solved (see Question 3 in the exercises). So the neighborhood of any vertex looks like a simple "cartwheel" with the center at the vertex, and at least three "spokes":

Let's take the vertex O in the graph that has the smallest degree. If the degree of O is 3, the problem is solved. Indeed, O is inside a triangle, and there must be no vertices outside (see Question 3 in the exercises). This means our graph is simply K_4:

If the degree of O is 4, we need a little more work, but not much.

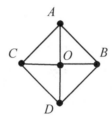

Let us "glue" the vertices B, O, and C together and properly color the resulting graph — we can do that by the induction hypothesis. When we unglue B, O, and C, all three will be colored in the same color, say color 1. The rest of the graph will be properly colored. Vertices A and D use at most two colors, say 2 and 3. Color 4 remains free, and we can recolor O in that color and get a proper coloring of our graph:

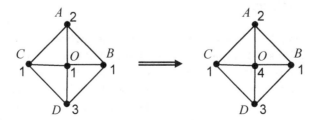

It turns out that any planar graph has a vertex of degree 5 or less (see Question 6 in the exercises). We have already considered the cases when the degree of O is 3 or 4. The only remaining case is when the degree of O is 5. This is the hardest case. If we remove O and the edges that connect it to its neighbors and add two "diagonals" to restore full triangulation, we get a smaller graph:

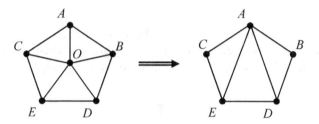

By the induction hypothesis, we can color this smaller graph in four colors. Unfortunately, A, B, C, D, and E, can use all four colors among them (see Figure 16-5).

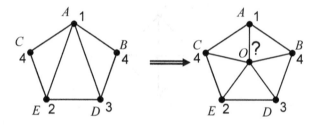

Figure 16-5. The worst case in the Kempe's proof: the neighbors of O use all four colors

There is no easy way to simply recolor O and get proper coloring. Perhaps we can somehow recolor one of the vertices A, D, or E, or recolor both B and C to free one of the colors and use it for O. But how? That's where Kempe's idea, known as *Kempe's chains*, comes in.

A Kempe's chain is a path in a properly colored graph whose vertices are colored in two colors. Consider a subgraph in a properly-colored graph that consists of all the vertices colored in a pair of colors, say 1 and 2, and all the edges that connect them. This subgraph is not necessarily connected: not all of its vertices are necessarily connected to each other by a 1-2-colored "chain" (path). If this 1-2-colored subgraph is not connected, it splits into several connectivity components. We can take one of these components and flip the colors in it: 1 into 2 and 2 into 1. If our original graph was properly colored, the new coloring will be also proper. This method allows us to recolor some of the vertices in a properly colored graph without disturbing the other vertices.

Let us see how this applies to our proof. If A and E (see Figure 16-5) are not connected by a 1-2 chain, we can take the largest connected 1-2 subgraph around A and flip the colors in it, without disturbing the colors of B, C, D, and E. A will be recolored from 1 to 2, and 1 will be freed to color O. Similarly, if there is no 1-3 chain from A to D, we can recolor A in color 3 and free 1 for O.

So far so good. The only situation that remains to consider is when there are both a 1-2 chain from A to E and a 1-3 chain from A to D. For example:

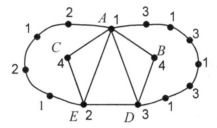

These chains serve as barriers on the plane between other pairs of vertices. The 1-2 chain from A to E ensures that there is no 4-3 chain from C to D, because 1-2 and 4-3 chains can't intersect. (If they did intersect in a vertex, what color would that vertex be?) So we can recolor C from 4 to 3. Likewise, we can recolor B from 4 to 2. 4 will be freed to color O.

This would complete our proof, if there weren't a big flaw, or, as mathematicians say, a "hole" in it. There is literally a hole in Kempe's chains: he didn't consider what "leaky" barriers they make. The 1-2 and 1-3 chains from A can take a round-about path to their destinations instead of the direct path shown above. They can intersect. The 4-2 and 4-3 chains can "leak" out their barriers and get "close" to each other, causing trouble: two vertices on these chains can be connected by an edge. Question 10 in the exercises asks you to provide a counterexample to Kempe's proof.

Exercises

1.   The map below has six regions (including the outer region). Draw a corresponding planar graph and properly color in four colors both the map and the graph.

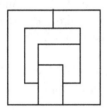

2.   Consider a graph

Draw the graph obtained from it by gluing A and B together. ✓

3.   Suppose we have a planar graph with n vertices. Suppose we know somehow (for example, from an induction hypothesis) that any planar graph with less than n vertices can be colored in p colors. Suppose also that our graph contains a "triangle" (a region bounded by three edges) with some vertices inside and some vertices outside. Prove that our graph can be colored in p colors, too. ✓

4. Convert the following graph into a fully triangulated graph by adding edges (but not vertices):

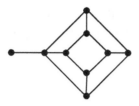

⹅ Hint: don't forget the infinite outer region: it should be a "triangle," too. ⹆ ✓

5.◆ One has to be very careful with math induction proofs. Consider the following "proof" of an obviously incorrect statement: Any graph can be properly colored in three colors.

1. <u>Base case</u>. The statement is obviously true for a graph with 3 or fewer vertices.

2. <u>Inductive case</u>. Suppose the statement is true for any graph with less than n vertices (inductive hypothesis); let us prove that then the statement is true for any graph with n vertices. Let's take a graph with n vertices. Let's take any two vertices that are not connected by an edge and glue them together. By the induction hypothesis, we can color the resulting graph in three colors. Now let's unglue the vertices back, preserving the coloring. The vertices that were glued have the same color, but that's OK, since they are not connected by an edge. The original graph is now properly colored, too.

Find a flaw in this "proof." ✓

6.◆ Prove that any planar graph has at least one vertex of degree 5 or lower.
⹅ Hints: it is sufficient to prove this for fully triangulated graphs; use Euler's formula that relates the number of vertices, edges, and regions in a planar graph: $V - E + R = 2$; estimate the number of edges in two ways: from the triangular regions and from the degrees of vertices. ⹆ ✓

7.◆ Give an example of a fully triangulated planar graph such that all its vertices have a degree of 5 or higher. What is the smallest number of vertices of degree 5 in such a graph? ✓

8. ▪   In the graph in Figure 16-4 take the vertex "in Oregon," colored in color 2, find its 2-3 component, and flip the colors in it.

9. ▪   Suppose O is a vertex in a fully triangulated graph and its degree is greater than or equal to four. Show that there are at least two neighbors of O that are not connected by an edge.

10. ◆   Complete the coloring of the graph below to make a counterexample to Kempe's "proof."

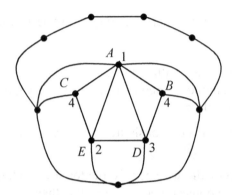

11. ◆   Prove the Five Color Theorem: any planar graph can be properly colored in five colors. ⸜ Hint: use the ideas from the "proof" of the Four Color theorem. ⸝

16.5 Review

Terms introduced in this chapter:

> *Adjacency matrix*
> *Planar graph*
> *Proper coloring*
> *Fully triangulated graph*
> *Four Color Theorem*
> *Kempe's chain*
> *Five Color Theorem*

17 Number Theory and Cryptology

17.1 Prologue

Number theory is a broadly defined branch of mathematics that deals with properties of numbers, especially integers. Many number theoretical concepts are easy to grasp: prime numbers, greatest common divisor, remainder, and so on. But some theorems are very difficult. You have probably heard of Fermat's Last Theorem, which states that the equation $a^n + b^n = c^n$ has no positive integer solutions for $n > 2$. This theorem was proposed by Pierre de Fermat in the 1630s. Fermat left a note in the margin of his copy of Diophantus's *Arithmetica* stating that he had a marvelous proof of this theorem, but the margin was too small to write it down. Three and a half centuries of futile attempts to prove the theorem led to many advances in number theory. Finally, Andrew Wiles of Princeton University presented a proof in 1993. Wiles' proof relied on earlier results that linked Fermat's Last Theorem to the properties of a certain class of elliptic curves. The proof took over seven years to complete and three lectures to present.[*]

In this chapter we will only scratch the surface. We will start with Euclid's algorithm for finding the greatest common divisor, which will lead us to the fundamental theorem of arithmetic. We will take that opportunity to present a mini-theory, with definitions, theorems, and proofs, to give you a taste of such things. We will then consider arithmetic operations on remainders and applications of number theory to cryptology, the science of ciphers.

17.2 Euclid's Algorithm

Given two integers, a and $d \neq 0$, we say that a is evenly divisible by d (or, simply, that a is divisible by d) if $a = qd$ for some integer q. We can also say that d divides a or that d is a *divisor* of a.

> We will consider only positive divisors: $d > 0$.

---

[*] It took Wiles another year and some help from his former student Richard Taylor to fill a gap discovered in his proof.

> **The notation $d \mid a$ means d divides a.**

If $d \mid a$ and $d \mid b$, then d is a *common divisor* of a and b. GCD(a, b) stands for the greatest common divisor of a and b. (Sometimes, the greatest common divisor is called the *greatest common factor*, GCF.) Finding the GCD of two numbers is a common mathematical operation; it is used, for example, for reducing fractions.

You can find the GCD(a, b) for positive a and b by simply trying every number d, starting from 2 and up to a or b, whichever is smaller, and testing whether d is a common divisor. Such a "brute-force" approach, however, gets pretty tedious for big numbers.

Over 2300 years ago, in Book VII of his *Elements*, Euclid described an efficient algorithm for finding the GCD. Euclid's algorithm is based on the following key observation: if $a > b > 0$, then GCD(a, b) = GCD($a - b$, b). (We leave the proof of this fact to you — see Question 1.) This allows us to go from a and b to smaller numbers, $a - b$ and b. We repeat this operation several times, each time choosing the larger of a and b to reduce. Sooner or later we come to the situation where $a = b$. Then, of course, GCD(a, b) = $a = b$.

Example 1

Using Euclid's algorithm, find GCD(18, 30)

Solution

GCD(18, 30) = GCD(18, 12) = GCD(6, 12) = GCD(6, 6) = 6

Example 2

Write a Python function that uses Euclid's algorithm to find and return the greatest common divisor of two positive integers.

Solution

```python
def gcd(a, b):
    while a != b:
        if a > b:
            a -= b
        else:
            b -= a
    return a              # or return b
```

> Two integers *a* and *b* are called *relatively prime* if they have no common divisors except 1, that is GCD(*a*, *b*) = 1.

The concept of relatively prime numbers and the idea of Euclid's algorithm help us analyze and solve equations of the type $ax + by = c$. Here *a*, *b*, and *c* are given integers, and a solution is a pair of integers *x* and *y*. This type of equation is called a *linear Diophantine equation in two variables*. In general, a polynomial equation in one or several variables is called a *Diophantine equation* if we are looking only for its integer solutions. Such equations are named after Diophantus, a Greek mathematician who lived in Alexandria in the 3rd century AD and studied equations with integer solutions. The first descriptions of linear Diophantine equations are found much earlier, in Indian texts that are 2800 years old.

Example 3

A classroom has several desks. When we arrange the desks in rows of 5, all the rows are complete, but when we arrange the desks in rows of 3, one desk remains:

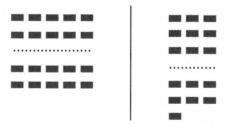

How many desks are there in the classroom, if their number is between 15 and 30?

Solution

If *D* is the number of desks, then $D = 5x$ and $D = 3y + 1$, where *x* and *y* are some positive integers. Then $5x = 3y + 1$, which leads to the Diophantine equation $5x - 3y = 1$.

This equation is easy to solve. We know that *D* is divisible by 5. We also know that $D \geq 15$. We start counting by 5 from 15: 15, 20, ... — and soon get the answer: $D = 25$. Indeed, when 25 is divided by 3, the remainder is 1. Here $x = 5$ and $y = 8$. If we keep going — 30, 35, ... — we soon get another number with the same properties, $D = 40$, but it is out of the given range.

Another way to solve this puzzle is to start from 1 and count by 3 until we get a number evenly divisible by 5 and within the 15-30 range: 1, 4, 7, 10, 13, 16, 19, 22, 25.

> **If the equation $ax + by = c$ has a solution, then it has infinitely many solutions, because if an x, y pair is a solution, then the $x + b$, $y - a$ pair is also a solution, the $x + 2b$, $y - 2a$ pair is a solution, and so on.**

Does an equation $ax + by = 1$, where a and b are integers, always have a solution? Does $6x - 4y = 1$, for example, have a solution? Of course not! The left side must be an even number, so it can't be 1. What about $14x + 21y = 1$? Here $a = 14$, $b = 21$, and they have a common divisor 7. Therefore, the left side is always divisible by 7, so it can't be equal to 1. In general, if a and b have a common divisor greater than 1, then the equation $ax + by = 1$ has no solutions. What if a and b have no common divisors other than 1?

Linear Diophantine Equation Theorem

An equation $ax + by = 1$, where a and b are integers, has an integer solution if and only if a and b are relatively prime.

Proof:

We have already shown that if a and b have a common divisor greater than 1, then the equation has no solutions. Now let's assume that a and b <u>are</u> relatively prime and show that a solution exists.

Note that 0 is not relatively prime with any number, so we must have $a \neq 0$, $b \neq 0$. Without loss of generality we can assume that a and b are positive: if they are not, we can adjust the sign of x and/or y accordingly. For example, $ax + by = 1$ can be rewritten as $ax + (-b)(-y) = 1$. Also, a and b can't be equal, unless $a = b = 1$.

The main idea of the proof is the same as in Euclid's algorithm. Suppose $a > b$. Then $ax + by = 1$ can be rewritten as $(a - b)x + b(x + y) = 1$ or $(a - b)x_2 + by_2 = 1$. The original equation has a solution if and only if the new equation, with the coefficients $(a - b)$ and b, has a solution. $(a - b)$ and b are still positive and relatively prime. If we repeat this procedure several times, always subtracting the smaller coefficient from the larger one, we get smaller and smaller coefficients, until we come to $a = 1$, $b = 1$. Obviously the equation $x + y = 1$ has solutions (for example, $x = 1$, $y = 0$ or $x = 2$, $y = -1$). So the original equation must have a solution, too. Q.E.D.

Figure 17-1 illustrates the above proof for the equation $5x - 3y = 1$.

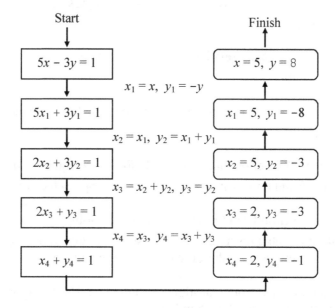

Figure 17-1. Finding a solution of a linear Diophantine equation by repeatedly reducing its coefficients

Exercises

1.   Show that if $a > b > 0$, then GCD(a, b) = GCD(a - b, b). ✓

2.   Write a Python function `gcd(a, b)` that calculates the greatest common divisor of two positive integers a and b by using a "brute-force" approach: just check whether both a and b are divisible by d for all d from 2 to `min(a,b)`. ⸨ Hint: it is more efficient to go from `min(a,b)` down to 1. ⸩

3.   Rewrite the `gcd` function from Example 2 recursively, without loops.

4. ■ The gcd function in Example 2 can be made more efficient. If $a > b$, instead of subtracting b from a multiple times, we can replace a with the remainder of the division of a by b (using Python's modulo division operator). The same for $b > a$. Write and test this more efficient version of the gcd function. ⸮ Hint: make sure your code acts properly when a becomes divisible by b or b becomes divisible by a. ⸮ Compare the running times for the original and the modified code for $a = 18289894500228625200$, $b = 14814814692$.

5. Show that if a and b are relatively prime, then the equation $ax + by = c$ has an integer solution for any c. ✓

6. ■ Show that $ax + by = c$ has an integer solution if and only if c is divisible by $GCD(a, b)$.

7. Write and test a function that finds a solution of the equation $ax + by = 1$ for given a and b and returns it as a tuple. Use the approach of Example 3.

8. Modify the function from Question 7 to find the solution of $ax + by = 1$ with the smallest possible positive integer x. Write another version of this function that returns the solution with x in a given range.

9. Rewrite the function from Question 7 recursively. Use the approach outlined in the proof of the linear Diophantine equation theorem.

10. Show that if p and q are two different primes, any arithmetic sequence with the common difference p has a term that is divisible by q.

11. ■ Show that there is no prime that divides all Fibonacci numbers, starting from a certain place in the sequence.

12. Is it true that if $GCD(a, b) = 1$ or $GCD(b, c) = 1$ or $GCD(c, a) = 1$, then the greatest common factor of a, b and c is 1? If so, prove it; if not give a counterexample. Is the converse true? If so, prove it; if not give a counterexample.

13. ◆ Formulate and prove the necessary and sufficient condition for the equation $ax + by + cz = 1$ to have an integer solution. ✓

17.3 The Fundamental Theorem of Arithmetic

In this section we present a mini-theory that leads to the fundamental theorem of arithmetic. We present it in the typical mathematical style with definitions and theorems. To make our theory complete, we restate here the definitions from Section 17.2.

Definition 1:

Let n be an integer. A positive integer d is called its *divisor* if there exists an integer q such that $n = qd$.

Definition 2:

An integer p is called a *prime* if $p > 1$ and p has no divisors other than 1 and p.

Definition 3:

Two integers m and n are called *relatively prime* if they have no common divisors greater than 1.

Theorem 1:

Any integer greater than 1 is either a prime or can be represented as a product of primes.

Proof:

This is a proof by mathematical induction.
Base case: The statement is true for $n = 2$, because 2 is a prime.
Induction hypothesis: Suppose that the statement is true for any integer greater than 1 and less than n. Now let's show that the statement is then true for n. Indeed, if n is a prime, the statement is true for n. If n is <u>not</u> a prime, then $n = qd$, where $1 < d < n$ and $1 < q < n$. By the induction hypothesis, d is a prime or a product of primes. The same for q. Combining the products for q and d into one product we conclude that n is a product of primes, too. By mathematical induction, the statement is true for any $n \geq 2$, Q.E.D.

A slightly different take on this proof relies on the fact that any non-empty set of positive integers has a smallest number. (This fact is equivalent to math induction.) Consider the set of all numbers greater than 1 for which the statement is <u>not</u> true. If this set is empty, our proof is complete. If not, let n be its smallest element. n can't be a prime, so $n = qd$, where $1 < d < n$ and $1 < q < n$. Since n is the smallest number for which the statement is false, the statement must be true for q and d. But if we factor both d and q into primes, and combine them into one product, we get n. So the statement must also be true for n. This is a contradiction, so no such n can exist.

| A *corollary* is a mathematical fact that easily follows from a theorem.

Corollary:

There are infinitely many primes.

Proof:

Suppose the set of all primes were finite: $p_1, p_2, ..., p_n$. Consider $n = p_1 \cdot p_2 \cdot ... \cdot p_n + 1$. By Theorem 1, n must be a prime or have a prime divisor. That prime must be different from any of the $p_1, p_2, ..., p_n$ because none of the p_i is a divisor of n. This is a contradiction, so our assumption that the set of all primes is finite was false.

Theorem 2:

If integers a and b are relatively prime, then there exist integers x and y, such that $ax + by = 1$.

Proof:

This is a part of the linear Diophantine equation theorem from Section 17.2.

Theorem 3:

If p is a prime and $p \mid mn$, then $p \mid m$ or $p \mid n$.

This is Proposition 30 in Book VII of Euclid's *Elements*. It is also known as *Euclid's First Theorem*. The statement seems completely obvious, but its proof is not obvious at all. This is common in mathematics.

Proof:

This is a proof by contradiction. Suppose p divides neither m nor n. Then p and n are relatively prime (because p is a prime). By Theorem 2, there exist integers x and y such that $px + ny = 1$. Multiplying both sides by m we get $mpx + mny = m$. The left side is divisible by p, because $p \mid mn$. So m must be divisible by p, too. Therefore, our assumption that p divides neither m nor n was false. Q.E.D.

Corollary:

If p is a prime and $p \mid n_1 \cdot \ldots \cdot n_k$, then $p \mid n_1$ or $p \mid n_2$ or ... or $p \mid n_k$.

Proof:

By Theorem 3, $p \mid n_1$ or $p \mid n_2 \cdot \ldots \cdot n_k$. etc.

We are now ready to tackle the fundamental theorem of arithmetic.

Theorem 4 (the fundamental theorem of arithmetic):

Any integer greater than 1 can be represented as a product of primes, and such factorization is unique (if we disregard the order of factors).

Proof:

By Theorem 1, any integer greater than 1 is either a prime or a product of primes. Now we have to show that such factorization is unique. Suppose there exist numbers with two different factorizations. Let's take the smallest such number $n = p_1 \cdot ... \cdot p_i = q_1 \cdot ... \cdot q_j$. $q_1 | n$, so $q_1 | p_1 \cdot ... \cdot p_i$. By Theorem 3, q_1 must be one of the primes $p_1, ..., p_i$. Therefore, we can divide $p_1 \cdot ... \cdot p_i$ and $q_1 \cdot ... \cdot q_j$ by q_1 and get a smaller number n / q_1 with two different factorizations. This is a contradiction, so no such n can exist.

Exercises

1. Prove that for any positive integer k there are k consecutive positive integers, such that none of them is a prime. ⸢ Hint: start at $(k+1)! + 2$. ⸣

2. 7, 13, 19 form an arithmetic sequence and they are all primes. Show that an infinite arithmetic sequence cannot contain only primes. ⸢ Hint: see Question 1. ⸣

3.■ Write and test a program that prompts the user to enter an integer n greater than 1 and prints all its prime factors in ascending order. Each factor must be printed as many times as it appears in the factorization of n. The dialog with the program should look like this:

    ```
    Enter an integer greater than 1: 90
    90 = 2*3*3*5
    ```

    or

    ```
    Enter an integer greater than 1: 3
    3 = 3
    ```

4. If $p_1, p_2, ..., p_n$ are the first n primes, is it always true that $p_1 \cdot p_2 \cdot .... \cdot p_n + 1$ is a prime? If you believe it is true, prove it. If not, find a counterexample.

5. Write a program to find the smallest positive n such that $n^2 - n + 41$ is <u>not</u> a prime. (There is no polynomial, even in several variables, that produces only prime values.)

6. Show that any prime greater than 2 can be uniquely represented as $a^2 - b^2$, where a and b are positive integers. ✓

7. Write a program to find the biggest prime among the first 100 Fibonacci numbers. (Mathematicians don't yet know whether there are infinitely many primes among Fibonacci numbers.)

8. *Goldbach's conjecture* states that every even integer greater than 2 can be represented as the sum of two primes. For example, $12 = 5 + 7$. It is not known whether this conjecture is true or false. Write a program to verify Goldbach's conjecture for all even numbers from 4 to 100.

9. Show that the number of different divisors of n is even, unless n is a perfect square. The number of different divisors of a perfect square is odd.

10. Suppose $n = p_1^{j_1} \cdot ... \cdot p_k^{j_k}$, where $p_1, ..., p_k$ are different primes. Express the total number of divisors of n in terms of $j_1, ..., j_k$.

11. Suppose $n = p^{j_1} \cdot q^{j_2}$, where p and q are two different primes. Show that the number of positive integers that are less than n and are relatively prime with n is $n\left(1 - \dfrac{1}{p}\right)\left(1 - \dfrac{1}{q}\right)$. Extend the result for three primes; for any number of primes.

17.4 Arithmetic of Remainders

Let n and d be integers and $d > 0$. We can divide n by d with a remainder. This means that we can find integers q and r, such that $n = qd + r$, where $0 \le r < d$. Here q is the quotient and r is the remainder.

> **Two integers *m* and *n* are said to be *congruent modulo d*, if they give the same remainder when divided by *d*. This is written as $m \equiv n \pmod{d}$.**
>
> ***n* mod *d* denotes the remainder when *n* is divided by *d*.**

For example, $12 \equiv 27 \pmod 5$: both 12 and 27 give the same remainder when divided by 5: 12 mod 5 = 27 mod 5 = 2.

If $m \equiv n \pmod{d}$, then $d \mid (m - n)$, that is, $m - n$ is divisible by d.

Congruence modulo d is an *equivalence relation* on integers (see Section 15.3). Indeed, all three required criteria for an equivalence relation are satisfied:

1. Reflexivity: $n \equiv n \pmod{d}$
2. Symmetry: If $m \equiv n \pmod{d}$, then $n \equiv m \pmod{d}$
3. Transitivity: If $k \equiv m \pmod{d}$ and $m \equiv n \pmod{d}$, then $k \equiv n \pmod{d}$

Therefore, for a given d, all integers fall into non-overlapping equivalence classes with respect to congruence modulo d. Two integers from the same class give the same remainder when divided by d, and two integers from different classes give different remainders. The number of congruence classes is d.

Example 1

List the congruence classes modulo 3.

Solution

There are three classes:

$$\{\ldots -12, -9, -6, -3, 0, 3, 6, 9, 12, \ldots\} \equiv 0 \pmod{3}$$
$$\{\ldots -11, -8, -5, -2, 1, 4, 7, 10, 13, \ldots\} \equiv 1 \pmod{3}$$
$$\{\ldots -10, -7, -4, -1, 2, 5, 8, 11, 14, \ldots\} \equiv 2 \pmod{3}$$

❖   ❖   ❖

If we take any integer k and add it to all numbers in a congruence class modulo d, all of them will shift into another congruence class. For example, –4, 5, and 14 all belong to the "2" congruence class modulo 3. If we add 7 to each of them, we get 3, 12, and 21, all of which belong to the "0" congruence class. This is so, because $(n + k) \bmod d$ and $n \bmod d + k \bmod d$ are congruent modulo d:

$$[(n + k) \bmod d] \equiv [n \bmod d + k \bmod d] \pmod{d}$$

The same is true for multiplication:

$$[(n \cdot k) \bmod d] \equiv [n \bmod d \cdot k \bmod d] \pmod{d}$$

All of this means that we can add and multiply two congruence classes, or more precisely, any two representatives of these congruence classes. The result falls into the same class, regardless of which representatives we chose.

From now on, we will represent each congruence class modulo d simply by all possible remainders when n is divided by d: $0, 1, 2, ..., d-1$. Let's use the symbol $\oplus_d$ to denote addition modulo d. The sum of two numbers modulo d simply "wraps around" at d. It is as if the number line was wrapped around a circle with the numbers $0, 1, 2, ..., d-1$ evenly spaced on it (Figure 17-2). We are all familiar with such an arrangement on a clock, which adds hours modulo 12 (or modulo 24 on a European digital clock) and adds minutes modulo 60. The only difference is that in math we usually go counterclockwise.

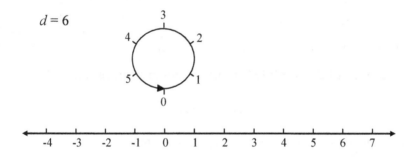

Figure 17-2. Addition and multiplication modulo d can be viewed as performed on a "number circle"

Example 2

$2 \oplus_3 2 = 4 \bmod 3 = 1$, is in the same congruence class as $5 \oplus_3 11 = 16 \bmod 3 = 1$.

Example 3

$7 \oplus_{12} 10 = 17 \bmod 12 = 5$

The same principle is used for multiplication. We will use the $\otimes_d$ symbol to denote multiplication modulo d.

Example 4

$2 \otimes_3 2 = 4 \mod 3 = 1$

$3 \otimes_5 4 = 12 \mod 5 = 2$

$7 \otimes_{12} 10 = 70 \mod 12 = 10$

❖   ❖   ❖

Figure 17-3 shows modulo 5 addition and multiplication tables.

$\oplus_5$	0	1	2	3	4		$\otimes_5$	0	1	2	3	4
0	0	1	2	3	4		0	0	0	0	0	0
1	1	2	3	4	0		1	0	1	2	3	4
2	2	3	4	0	1		2	0	2	4	1	3
3	3	4	0	1	2		3	0	3	1	4	2
4	4	0	1	2	3		4	0	4	3	2	1

Figure 17-3.   Modulo 5 addition and multiplication tables

❖   ❖   ❖

Modulo d arithmetic is similar in many ways to arithmetic on integers:

- It obeys the associative and commutative laws for addition and subtraction;
- It obeys the distributive law;
- There is a 0;
- There is a 1.
- Each element x has an additive inverse element y, such that $x \oplus_d y = 0$ (namely, $y = d - x$).

But there is a peculiarity, too: if d is <u>not</u> a prime, then you can find x and y such that $x \neq 0$, $y \neq 0$, but $x \otimes_d y = 0$. For example, $2 \otimes_6 3 = 0$. Such x and y are called *divisors of zero*.

If p is a prime, then multiplication modulo p has no divisors of zero. Moreover, for each $x \neq 0$ there is a y such that $x \otimes_p y = 1$. For example, take a look at the multiplication table in Figure 17-3: $2 \otimes_5 3 = 1$. Every row of the table has a 1. We can say that in modulo p arithmetic, $y = \dfrac{1}{x}$. We can do division! So the arithmetic of remainders modulo p, for a prime p, is similar to the arithmetic of rational numbers.

Let's prove this fact: that in modulo p arithmetic any $x \neq 0$ has a reciprocal $y = \dfrac{1}{x}$. But first we need to review a couple of properties of exponents:

- $x^0 = 1$

- $x^m \cdot x^n = x^{m+n}$

Theorem 1:

Let p be a prime. For any $0 < x < p$, there exist a $0 < y < p$, such that $xy \equiv 1 \pmod p$.

Proof:

Consider the geometric sequence $1, x, x^2, x^3, \ldots$. Since there are only p different remainders modulo p, sooner or later two terms in this sequence will have the same remainder. Suppose $x^n \equiv x^m \pmod p$ where $n > m$. Then $x^n - x^m \equiv 0 \pmod p$. $x^n - x^m = x^m(x^{n-m} - 1)$ and p does not divide x^m (see Theorem 3 in Section 17.3). Therefore $x^{n-m} - 1 \equiv 0 \pmod p \Rightarrow x^{n-m} \equiv 1 \pmod p$. We can take $y = x^{n-m-1}$. Q.E.D.

If p is a prime and we take any $0 < a < p$ and look at the remainders of $1, a, a^2, a^3, \ldots$ modulo p, we can see that they form a periodic sequence (Figure 17-4). The period of the sequence always divides $p - 1$, and $a^{p-1} \equiv 1 \pmod p$.

mod 7	1	a	a^2	a^3	a^4	a^5	a^6	a^7
$a = 2$	1	2	4	1	2	4	1	2
$a = 3$	1	3	2	6	4	5	1	3
$a = 4$	1	4	2	1	4	2	1	4

**Figure 17-4. Remainders modulo p for a geometric sequence
form a periodic sequence (here $p = 7$)**

Theorem 2 (Fermat's Little Theorem):

For any positive integer a and a prime p, $a^p \equiv a \pmod{p}$.

Proof:

If $p \mid a$, then $a^p \equiv a \equiv 0 \pmod{p}$. If not, as we saw above $a^{p-1} \equiv 1 \pmod{p} \Rightarrow$ $a^p \equiv a \pmod{p}$.

Exercises

1. Explore what Python's n % d operator returns when $n < 0$ and/or $d < 0$.

2. Show that addition and multiplication modulo 2 corresponds to the XOR and AND operations, respectively, where FALSE is 0 and TRUE is 1.

3. Write and test a function elapsedTime that returns the time difference in minutes from (hour1, min1) to (hour2, min2). ✓

4.■ Suppose the days of the week are represented by numbers: Sunday — 0, Monday — 1, and so on. Write and test a function that takes the day of the week for January 1 and returns the date of Thanksgiving (fourth Thursday in November) for that year (assuming this is not a leap year).

5. Write by hand the addition and multiplication tables modulo 6. ✓

6. Show that there are two numbers in any set of 101 integers whose difference ends with two zeros.

7. Write and test a program that prompts the user to enter an integer d greater than 1 and prints out the addition and multiplication tables modulo d.

8. Show that if p is a prime and $p \mid a^2$ then $p^2 \mid a^2$.

9.■ Find the smallest positive n, such that $n \equiv 2 \pmod{3}$, $n \equiv 3 \pmod{4}$, $n \equiv 4 \pmod{5}$, and so on, $n \equiv 11 \pmod{12}$.

10.■ Calculate 3^{22222} mod 23 using pencil and paper only.

11.■ Show that for any positive n, $6 \mid n(n+1)(2n+1)$

12.■ Show that if p is a prime greater than or equal to 5, then $p^2 - 1$ is evenly divisible by 24.

13.■ Write and test a function that takes a positive integer a and a prime p and returns the smallest $k > 1$ such that $a^k - a \equiv 0 \pmod{p}$.

14. Show that if p and q are two different primes, and $0 \le a < p$ and $0 \le b < q$, you can find x such that $x \equiv a \pmod{p}$ and $x \equiv b \pmod{q}$. (This is a simple special case of the *Chinese remainder theorem*.) ⸮ Hint: see Question 10 in Section 17.2. ⸮

15. Wilson's theorem states that if p is a prime, $(p-1)! + 1$ is evenly divisible by p.

(a) Show that Wilson's theorem is true only for primes.

(b)♦ Prove Wilson's theorem. ⸮ Hint: recall that every x has a reciprocal $y = \dfrac{1}{x}$ modulo p, and that $x = y$ only for $x = 1$ and $x = p - 1$. ⸮ ✓

(c)■ Write and test a program that prints out the first 100 primes using Wilson's theorem.

16.♦ Fermat's little theorem can be used to test a number p for primeness: p is a prime if and only if $a^{p-1} \equiv 1 \pmod{p}$ for all positive a that are not divisible by p. We can choose several such values of a at random and test the condition; if it works for all of them, then the probability of p being a prime is very high. Write a function that takes a positive integer p and checks whether it is likely to be a prime by using up to 100 random values for a ($1 < a < p$). Using this function, find the first prime over 1,000,000. ⸮ Hint: recall that the `randint(a, b)` function from the `random` module returns a random integer from a to b (inclusive). ⸮

17.5 Number Theory in Cryptology

Cryptology is a science of making and analyzing ciphers. In a simple case, if Alice and Bob want to send each other encrypted messages, all they have to do is agree on which encryption method they are going to use. ("Alice" and "Bob" are often used in cryptology literature to explain secure communications between two people or organizations. There is a third character, eavesdropper "Eve," who monitors all exchanges between Alice and Bob. Eve will try to guess which method Alice and Bob are using.)

Example 1

The simplest substitution cipher: each letter is replaced with the next letter in the alphabet; 'Z' is replaced by 'A'. "Got an A" is encrypted as "Hpu bo B".

❖   ❖   ❖

This type of cipher is easy to break once many people start using the same method. In a more advanced cipher, the encryption method is widely known, but Alice and Bob share a secret *key*, which modifies the encryption scheme.

Example 2

In a simple substitution cipher, a secret key tells which letter should replace 'A', 'B', ..., 'Z'. For example:

Letter to encrypt: `ABCDEFGHIJKLMNOPQRSTUVWXYZ`
Key: `QEKUOYMBJXRCDZNVTGFASHWPLI`

"On time" is encrypted as "Nz ajdo." This cipher is easy to break by comparing the frequencies of occurrence of different letters in the plain text and encoded text and by guessing about the common short words (articles, prepositions, etc.).

❖   ❖   ❖

In a cipher that uses a secret key, Alice and Bob must somehow share the key. They can meet or send a sealed envelope by snail mail. This might work if *A* and *B* are just two people. But what if *A* is Amazon.com and *B* is any customer who wants to place a book order in a secure manner? Imagine 100,000,000 Internet customers and 100,000 secure servers at e-commerce sites. You would need to distribute

10,000,000,000,000 different keys to allow each to communicate with each! To address this problem, companies use several very clever schemes that emerged in the 1970s. We will consider two of them: *Diffie-Hellman Key Exchange* and, in the following section, *RSA public/private key encryption*.

The Diffie-Hellman Scheme

The Diffie-Hellman Key Exchange algorithm was invented by Whitfield Diffie and Martin Hellman. The key idea (pun intended!) of the D-H scheme is to let each member of the community own "one half" of a key. All these half-keys are public, either published in a directory or available upon request from the owner. Any two halves can be put together to make a unique key. However, the person combining the two halves must know the secret code for at least one of the halves to be able to join them together. Alice has a secret code to her half and Bob has a secret code to his half, so either Alice or Bob can put together their halves to make a complete key; the resulting key will be the same. But Eve cannot put together Alice's and Bob's half-keys (Figure 17-5).

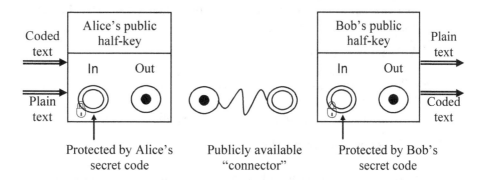

Figure 17-5. A metaphor for the D-H scheme: Alice's and Bob's half-keys are publicly available, but you need to know either Alice's or Bob's secret code to combine them into a complete key suitable for encoding and decoding messages.

In the numerical model of this scheme, Alice's public half-key is $K_A = r^a \bmod p$, Bob's public half-key is $K_B = r^b \bmod p$, and the combined key is $K = r^{ab} \bmod p$, where p and r are in the public domain and are used by everyone. p is a large prime: it is chosen to have about 200 digits! $1 < r < p$.

In modulo p arithmetic, it is virtually impossible to calculate K from K_A and K_B for a very large p, unless you know a or b. It is also virtually impossible to find a from K_A or b from K_B. But if you know a or b, combining K_A and K_B into one key K is easy. Recall the property of exponents: $\left(r^a\right)^b = r^{ab}$ (see Question 4). Likewise, $\left(r^b\right)^a = r^{ab}$. So $K = \left(K_B\right)^a = \left(K_A\right)^b$.

Here are the steps Alice takes to send a coded message to Bob:

1. Alice knows the standard p and r from the public domain.

2. Alice requests K_B from Bob.

3. Alice makes the encryption key $K = \left(K_B\right)^a \bmod p = r^{ab} \bmod p$ using her secret number a.

4. Alice encodes the plain text message M into the encoded message C using K as the key for encryption: $C = \text{encode}(M, K)$. (It is assumed that everyone is using the same encryption method — only the keys are different.)

5. Alice sends C to Bob.

Bob takes similar steps to decode the message received from Alice:

1. Bob knows the standard p and r from the public domain.

2. Bob requests K_A from Alice.

3. Bob makes the encryption key $K = \left(K_A\right)^b \bmod p = r^{ab} \bmod p$ using his secret number b.

4. Bob decodes C using K: $M = \text{decode}(C, K)$.

In regular arithmetic, if you know r and r^a, it is very easy to calculate a. For example, if $r = 10$, and $r^a = 1000$, you know right away that $a = 3$.

> **If $r^a = x$, then a is called the *logarithm of x to the base r*. It is written as $a = \log_r x$.**

In regular arithmetic, $\log_r x$ increases in a predictable way when x increases, which makes it easy to compute. Not so in modulo p arithmetic. When a changes from 1 to $p-1$, r^a mod p jumps around in the range from 1 to $p-1$.

$a = \log_r x \pmod{p}$ **is called the *discrete logarithm.***

Example 3

Find $\log_6 8 \pmod{11}$, that is, find a such that $6^a \equiv 8 \pmod{11}$.

Solution

Make a table of powers of 6 modulo 11:

a	0	1	2	3	4	5	6	7	8	9	10
6^a mod 11	1	6	3	7	9	10	5	8	4	2	1

An entry in the bottom row is the previous entry times 6 (mod 11). For example $6 \cdot 6 = 36 \equiv 3 \pmod{11}$; $3 \cdot 6 = 18 \equiv 7 \pmod{11}$. Look in the bottom row for the power of 6 that is equal to 8 and mark the corresponding a — here it is $a = 7$. Therefore, $\log_6 8 \pmod{11} = 7$.

Can't we make and search a similar table for any r and p? Not if p has 200 digits! We can always find r such that all the powers of r modulo p are different. Then the table of powers of r will have about 10^{200} columns! This is more than the number of atoms in the universe... squared! If we combine all the computers in the world (including all play stations[*]) and make them search for a discrete logarithm, it will take more time than the age of the universe... cubed!

---

[*] In the fall of 2007, The Guinness Book of Records recognized folding@home (FAH) as the world's most powerful distributed computing network. FAH has signed up more than 670,000 PS3 play stations to analyze, during their idle hours, the shapes of proteins and their effect on various diseases. The network is estimated to perform 10^{15} floating-point operations per second.

> **The discrete logarithm is virtually impossible to compute for very large p.**

On the other hand, calculating r^a is relatively quick, even for a very large a. For example, you need to perform only 10 multiplications to calculate r^{1024} (see Question 6).

The RSA Algorithm

The name of the RSA algorithm is formed by the first letters Ron Rivest, Adi Shamir, and Leonard Adleman at MIT, who invented the algorithm in 1977, independently of previous work.[**] The RSA algorithm is now widely used for secure communications and e-commerce on the Internet.

The main idea of the RSA scheme is simple. Suppose Alice wants to send a secret message to Bob. Alice asks Bob to send her an open padlock to which only Bob has a key. (Bob, like every other member of the community, has an unlimited supply of such locks and sends them out for free on request.) When Alice receives the lock, she puts her message in a box, puts the lock on it, clicks it locked, and sends the box to Bob.

In the numerical implementation, Bob sends to Alice, over an open channel, two numbers, E and N. These numbers together serve as the "lock" (but they are called Bob's public encryption key). Alice's message is stored in a computer as a sequence of 0s and 1s, and the RSA algorithm treats these bits as binary digits of a positive integer M. Alice "puts a lock" on M, that is, creates a coded message $C = M^E \bmod N$ and sends C back to Bob. Bob uses his secret private key D to decode C and get back M: $M = C^D \bmod N$.

For this to work, we must have $C^D \equiv \left(M^E\right)^D \equiv M^{ED} \equiv M \pmod{N}$, for any positive integer M. How is this possible?

[**] British mathematician Clifford Cocks, who worked for a UK intelligence agency, described a similar algorithm in 1973 in a top-secret internal paper. His discovery remained unknown until 1997.

Recall Fermat's little theorem (Section 17.4), which states that if p is a prime, then $x^p \equiv x \pmod{p}$, for any positive integer x. This is our starting point. If x is relatively prime with p, then $x^{p-1} \equiv 1 \pmod{p}$, which means $p \mid (x^{p-1} - 1)$.

The RSA scheme relies on a more general theorem. In RSA, N is not a prime but a product of two different primes: $N = p \cdot q$. p and q are chosen to be very large primes, at least 100 digits each, so N has at least 200 digits (over 640 binary digits). It is easy to calculate $N = p \cdot q$ but it is virtually impossible to factor N if p and q are kept secret — it would take forever.

The math needed to get $M^{ED} \equiv M \pmod{N}$ is a little long but elegant:

1. We limit M to $M < p$ and $M < q$. Then M is relatively prime to p and to q. So is any power of M.

2. Applying Fermat's little theorem to $x = M^{y(q-1)}$ and p, where y is any positive integer, we get $p \mid \left(\left(M^{y(q-1)} \right)^{p-1} - 1 \right) \Rightarrow$ $p \mid (M^{y(q-1)(p-1)} - 1)$. Similarly, $q \mid (M^{y(p-1)(q-1)} - 1)$.

3. Since both p and q are divisors of $M^{y(p-1)(q-1)} - 1$, their product N is also a divisor: $N \mid (M^{y(p-1)(q-1)} - 1)$. Therefore $M^{y(p-1)(q-1)} \equiv 1 \pmod{N}$. Multiplying both sides by M we get $M^{y(p-1)(q-1)+1} \equiv M \pmod{N}$.

4. All of the above are well-known results in number theory. Now all we need is to represent $y(p-1)(q-1)+1$ as a product ED. Bob chooses such E that it is relatively prime with $p-1$ and $q-1$. Then E is relatively prime with $(p-1)(q-1)$. Solving the Diophantine equation $Ex - (p-1)(q-1)y = 1$ (see Section 17.2), we find x and y and set $D = x$. Then $y(p-1)(q-1)+1 = ED$.

5. We have found D and E, such that $M^{ED} \equiv M \pmod{N}$ for any M relatively prime with N (in particular, for any M such that $M < p$ and $M < q$).

Eve knows only $N = pq$ and E, but not p and q. She can't factor N or compute $(p-1)(q-1)$, so she can't compute D.

The RSA scheme is a little slow, so, in practice, it is used only to send a secret key for a different cipher. Once both Alice and Bob know that secret key, they can communicate in that cipher.

Exercises

1. Write and test two functions, `encode(text, key)` and `decode(code, key)`, that implement a substitution cipher with a key. `text`, `code`, and `key` are strings, and each of the functions returns a string.

2. Write and test a function `letterCounts(text)` that calculates how many times each letter of the alphabet occurs in `text` and returns a list of these 26 counts.

3. Find on the Internet a description of the Vigenere cipher. Write and test `encode(text, key)` and `decode(code, key)` that use that cipher.

4. Show that for positive integers a and b, $\left(r^a\right)^b = r^{ab}$.

5. Write and test an efficient iterative function (no recursion) that performs only d multiplications to calculate $r^{\left(2^d\right)}$. Do not use `**`, `pow`, or any other Python built-in functions.

6.■ Calculate 3^{2013} without using the `**` operator, the `pow` function, or any other Python built-in function, in such a way that multiplication is performed fewer than 60 times total. { Hint: write an efficient iterative function to calculate r^a. Recall that $a = d_k \cdot 2^k + ... + d_1 \cdot 2 + d_0$, where $d_k, ..., d_0$ are binary digits of a, and see Question 5. }

7. Write and test a function that calculates and returns $r^a \bmod p$ in such a way that no intermediate result ever exceeds rp.

8.♦ $p = 170141183460469231731687303715884105727$ is a prime.
$a = 618970019642690137449562111$.
$r = 5$.
Calculate $r^a \bmod p$. { Hint: write an efficient function for $r^a \bmod p$; see Questions 6 and 7. }

9.■   Write and test a <u>recursive</u> function that uses a divide-and-conquer algorithm to calculate r^a mod p efficiently.

10.■ $p = 31, r = 3$.

(a)   Write and test a function `generatePublicKeys(secretCodes)` that takes a list of secret codes for several users and generates and returns a list of public half-keys for them in the D-H scheme. For example, `generatePublicKeys([3, 7, 4])` should return `[27, 17, 19]`. ⸜ Hint: use your function from Question 9 and a list comprehension. ⸝

(b)   Write a function `encode(msg, a, kB)` that encodes a message from Alice to Bob according to the D-H scheme using her secret code a and his public half-key kB. Assume that `msg` is a number, and simply use `msg ^ k` (bit-wise xor with the key) to encode it. The function should return a number that corresponds to the encoded message.

(c)   Write a function `decode(code, b, kA)` that decodes a message from Alice to Bob according to the D-H scheme using his secret code b and her public half-key kA. The function should return the decoded message.

(d)   Test the `encode` and `decode` functions. For example, `encode(9, 3, 17)` should return 6, and `decode(6, 7, 27)` should return 9.

11.   Show that if $x \equiv a \pmod{p}$ and $x \equiv a \pmod{q}$, then $x \equiv a \pmod{pq}$.

12.   In the RSA algorithm, given $p = 13$, $q = 17$, and $E = 5$, find D.

13.   In describing RSA, we used a metaphor of Bob sending an open lock to Alice and Alice sending Bob a secret message in a box locked by that lock. Suppose only locked boxes are allowed in the mail. Can Alice still send a secret message to Bob? ⸜ Hint: two locks can fit on a box. ⸝

17.6 Review

Terms and notation introduced in this chapter:

Number theory	*Divisors of 0*	$p \mid a$
Remainder	*Fermat's little theorem*	$\text{GCD}(a, b)$
Divisor	*Substitution cipher*	$a \equiv b \pmod{d}$
GCD	*Diffie-Hellman scheme*	$\log_r x$
Euclid's algorithm	*Properties of exponents:*	
Relatively prime numbers	$r^a \cdot r^b = r^{a+b}$	
Diophantine equation	$\left(r^a\right)^b = r^{ab}$	
The fundamental theorem		
of arithmetic	*Discrete logarithm*	
Corollary	*The RSA algorithm*	
Congruence modulo d		

Appendix A. Getting Started with Python

This appendix is on the Internet at:

`www.skylit.com/python`

Appendix B. Selected Functions: Built-In, Math, and Random

`help(obj)`	displays help for a function or module
`input(s)`	displays `s` as a prompt, then reads a line of text, typed in by the user, and returns it as a string
`abs(x)`	returns the absolute value of `x`
`max(a, b)`	returns the largest of a, b
`min(a, b)`	returns the smallest of a, b
`int(s)`	converts a string or a `float` into an integer
`round(x)`	rounds `x` to an integer
`round(x, n)`	rounds `x` to a floating point number with n digits after the decimal point
`float(s)`	converts a string or an `int` into a `float`
`str(n)`	converts n into a string
`bin(n)`	returns a string that represents n in binary
`hex(n)`	returns a string that represents n in hex
`oct(n)`	returns a string that represents n in octal
`len(s)`	returns the length of a string, list, or tuple
`sum(lst)`	returns the sum of the numbers from a list or tuple
`max(lst)`	returns the largest element of a list or tuple
`min(lst)`	returns the smallest element of a list or tuple
`list(s)`	converts a string or tuple into a list
`tuple(s)`	converts a string or list into a tuple
`range(n)`	generates 0, ..., n-1, as in: `for i in range(n):`
`open(pathname)`	opens a file
`open(pathname, 'w')`	creates a file and opens it for writing

from math import *		from random import *	
pi	3.14159...	x = random()	$0 \leq x < 1$
e	2.71828...	r = randint(a, b)	$a \leq r \leq b$
sqrt(x)	$\sqrt{x}$	a = choice(s)	s[r]
pow(x, y)	x^y	shuffle(lst)	shuffles lst
exp(x)	e^x		

Appendix C. String Operations and Methods

Contents type

The following methods return `True` if all the characters in s belong to the corresponding category; otherwise return `False`:	
s.isalpha()	Checks whether all the characters in s are letters
s.isdigit()	Checks whether all the characters in s are digits
s.isalnum()	Checks whether each character in s is either a letter or a digit
s.isupper()	Checks whether all the letters in s are upper case
s.islower()	Checks whether all the letters in s are lower case
s.isspace()	Checks whether all characters in s are "white space" (spaces, tabs, newline, etc.)

Examples:

```
>>> 'ab7'.isalpha()
False
>>> 'ab7'.isdigit()
False
>>> 'ab7'.isalnum()
True
>>> 'ab7'.isupper()
False
>>> 'ab7'.islower()
True
>>> ' * '.isspace()
False
>>> ' \n'.isspace()
True
```

Length and substrings

`len(s)`	Returns the number of characters in `s`
`ch = s[i]`	Sets `ch` to the *i*-th character in `s`
`s2 = s[i:j]`	Sets `s2` to the substring of `s` from `i` to `j-1`

Examples:

```
>>> len('abcd')
4
>>> 'abcd'[1]
'b'
```

```
>>> 'abcd'[1:3]
'bc'
>>> 'abcd'[:3]
'abc'
```

Search

The following methods return an `int`:	
`s.find(sub)`	Returns the index of the first occurrence of `sub` in `s`; if `sub` is not found, returns `-1`
`s.rfind(sub)`	Returns the index of the last occurrence of `sub` in `s`
`s.count(sub)`	Returns the number of times `sub` occurs in `s`
`s.find(sub, start, end)` `s.rfind(sub, start, end)` `s.count(sub, start, end)`	The versions with optional arguments `start`, `end`, look for `sub` only within the substring of `s` between `start` and `end-1`

Examples:

```
>>> 'never'.find('e')
1
>>> 'never'.find('x')
-1
>>> 'never'.rfind('e')
3
>>> 'never'.count('e')
2
```

```
>>> 'never'.find('ver')
2
>>> 'never'.find('e',2,4)
3
>>> 'never'.rfind('e',1,3)
1
>>> 'never'.find('ver',2,4)
-1
```

Case conversions

The following methods return a new string:	
`s.upper()`	All the letters are converted to upper case
`s.lower()`	All the letters are converted to lower case
`s.capitalize()`	The first letter is converted to upper case

Examples:

```
>>> 'ab7'.upper()
'AB7'
>>> 'Ab7'.lower()
'ab7'
>>> 'ab7'.capitalize()
'Ab7'
>>> '7ab'.capitalize()
'7ab'
```

Editing

The following methods return a new string:	
`s.replace(old, new)`	Replaces every occurrence of `old` in `s` with `new`
`s.strip()`	Removes white space at the beginning and at the end of `s`

Examples:

```
>>> '1*2*3'.replace('*','--')
'1--2--3'
>>> ' ab   \n'.strip()
'ab'
```

Parsing

The following methods return a list:	
`s.split(delim)`	returns a list of substrings separated by occurrences of `delim` in `s`
`s.splitlines()`	returns a list of lines in `s` — the same as `s.split('\n')`.

Examples:

```
>>> 'Line1\nLine 2'.splitlines()        >>> '1, 2, 3'.split(', ')
['Line1', 'Line 2']                     ['1', '2', '3']
```

Formatting

The following methods return a new string:	
`s.format(value,...)`	Formats `value` (or several values according to the `format` fields in `s`
`s.ljust(w, fill)`	Left-justifies `s` within a string of length `w` and pads it on the right with the `fill` character (`fill` is optional: if not given, `ljust`, `rjust` and `center`, use the space character as the default)
`s.rjust(w, fill)`	Right-justifies `s` and pads it on left with `fill`
`s.center(w, fill)`	Positions `s` in the middle of a string of length `w` and pads it on both sides with `fill`
`s.zfill(w)`	Right-justifies the string and pads it with 0s on the left — the same as `s.rjust(w,'0')`

Examples:

```
>>> '{0:>4s}{1:7.2f}'.format('$',2.5)    >>> 'ab'.rjust(6)
'   $   2.50'                            '    ab'
>>> 'ab'.ljust(6, '*')                   >>> 'ab'.center(6)
'ab****'                                 '  ab  '
                                         >>> '12'.zfill(4)
                                         '0012'
```

Appendix D. List, Set, and Dictionary Operations and Methods

Lists

Method/Operation	Description
`len(lst)`	Returns the number of elements in `lst`
`x = lst[i]`	Sets `x` to the *i*-th element of `lst`
`lst[i] = x`	Sets the *i*-th element of `lst` to `x`
`del lst[i]`	Deletes the *i*-th element and decrements the indices of the subsequent elements by one
`del lst[i:j]`	Deletes the elements from *i* to *j*-1 and adjusts the indices of the subsequent elements
`lst2 = lst[i:j]`	Creates a copy of the specified slice from `lst` and assigns it to `lst2`
`lst2 = lst[:]`	Creates a copy of `lst` and assigns it to `lst2`
`lst.insert(i, x)`	Inserts `x` at index `i`, shifting the subsequent elements to the right by 1
`lst.append(x)`	Appends `x` at the end of `lst`
`lst.pop(i)`	Returns the *i*-th element and removes it from `lst`
`lst.pop()`	Returns the last element and removes it from `lst`
`lst.remove(x)`	Removes the first occurrence of `x` from `lst`; raises an exception if none found
`lst.index(x)`	Returns the index of the first occurrence of `x` in `lst`; raises an exception if none found
`lst.count(x)`	Returns the number of times `x` occurs in `lst`
`lst.reverse()`	Reverses the order of elements in `lst`; returns `None`
`lst.sort()`	Arranges the elements of `lst` in ascending order; returns `None`

Examples:

```
>>> lst=['A', 'C']
>>> lst
['A', 'C']
>>> lst.insert(1, 'B')
>>> lst
['A', 'B', 'C']
>>> lst.append('A')
>>> lst
['A', 'B', 'C', 'A']
>>> lst.insert(2, 'A')
>>> lst
['A', 'B', 'A', 'C', 'A']
>>> lst.count('A')
3
>>> del lst[2]
>>> lst
['A', 'B', 'C', 'A']
>>> lst.reverse()
>>> lst
['A', 'C', 'B', 'A']
>>> lst.index('A')
0
>>> lst.remove('A')
>>> lst
['C', 'B', 'A']
>>> lst.sort()
>>> lst
['A', 'B', 'C']
>>> lst.pop(1)
'B'
>>> lst
['A', 'C']
>>> lst.pop()
'C'
>>> lst
['A']
```

Sets

Method/Operation	Description
`len(s)`	Returns the number of elements in `s`
`s.copy()`	Returns a copy of `s`
`s.add(x)`	Adds `x` to `s`
`s.remove(x)`	Removes `x` from `s`; raises an exception if `x` is not in `s`
`s.discard(x)`	Removes `x` from `s`; has no effect if `x` is not in `s`
`s.pop()`	Removes and returns an arbitrary element from `s`
`s1.issubset(s2)`	Returns `True` if `s1` is a subset of `s2`
`s.update(s2)`	Adds all the elements from a list, tuple, or set `s2` to `s`

Examples:

```
>>> s = {'A', 'C'}
>>> s
{'A', 'C'}
>>> s.add('B')
>>> s
{'A', 'C', 'B'}
>>> s.remove('A')
>>> s
{'C', 'B'}
>>> s.discard('X')
>>> s
{'C', 'B'}
>>> s.pop()
'C'
>>> s
{'B'}
>>> s2 = set('ABCD')
>>> s2
{'A', 'C', 'B', 'D'}
```

```
>>> s.issubset(s2)
True
>>> s.add('X')
>>> s
{'X', 'B'}
>>> s.issubset(s2)
False
>>> s.update(s2)
>>> s
{'A', 'C', 'B', 'D', 'X'}
```

Dictionaries

Method/Operation	Description
`len(d)`	Returns the number of key-value pairs in d
`x = d[k]`	Sets x to the value associated with the key k in d; if k is not in d, raises a `KeyError` exception
`d[k] = x`	If the key k is in d, changes the value associated with k to x; if k is not in d, adds the `k:x` pair to d
`del d[k]`	Deletes the key k and the associated value from d
`d2 = d.copy()`	Creates a copy of d and assigns it to d2
`k in d`	Returns `True` if k is in d; otherwise returns `False`
`d.keys()`	Returns a `dict_keys` object that contains all the keys in d
`d.items()`	Returns a set (a `dict_items` object) of all (key, value) pairs in d
`d.update(d2)`	Adds all the key-value pairs from d2 to d
`d.get(k)` `d.get(k, dflt)`	The same as `d[k]`, but returns `None` (or the given default value) when k is not in d

Examples:

```
>>> d = {'K1':'V1', 'K2':'V2'}
>>> d.keys()
dict_keys(['K2', 'K1'])
>>> d.items()
dict_items([('K2', 'V2'), ('K1', 'V1')])
>>> 'K2' in d
True
>>> del d['K2']
>>> d
{'K1': 'V1'}
>>> 'K2' in d
False
>>> d['K2'] = 'V2'
>>> d
{'K2': 'V2', 'K1': 'V1'}
```

```
>>> d.get('K2')
'V2'
>>> d.get('X', 'oops')
'oops'
```

Index

```python
# This program demonstrates some elements
# of Python's syntax
# Author: H. Dumpty

def someFun(n):
    '''This function takes a positive integer n
       performs some mysterious calculations, and
       returns a positive integer'''
    k = 0
    lst = []   # empty list

    while n > 0:
        if n % 2 != 0:
            lst.append(k)   # or: lst += [k]
        k += 1      # same as: k = k + 1
        n //= 2     # integer division with truncation

    lst2 = [2 ** k for k in lst]   # list comprehension
    return sum(lst2)

n = -1

while n <= 0:
    s = input('Enter a positive integer: ')
    try:
        n = int(s)
    except ValueError:
        print('Invalid input')

r = someFun(n)
print('n =', n, end=' ')
print('r =', r)

# Three other ways to display the same output:

print('n =', n, 'r =', r)
print('n = {0:d}  r = {1:d}'.format(n, r))
print('n = ' + str(n) + '  r = ' + str(r))
```